Faith and Science

Adam Ford

Faith and Science

Questions to Consider

EPWORTH PRESS

0 7162 0531 9

First published 1999
by Epworth Press
20 Ivatt Way
Peterborough, PE3 7PG

Typeset by
Regent Typesetting, London
Printed and bound in Great Britain by
Biddles Ltd, Guildford and King's Lynn

For Rose

Contents

Preface

It is quite natural, and by no means uncommon, for there to be tension between parents and their growing children; particularly if the children are creative and headstrong, with their own ideas, wanting to go their own way. Science, the offspring of Western religion, has all the characteristics of a self-willed but creative child; stubborn, argumentative – and often right!

It is no accident that science was born in the West. The Jewish, Christian and Moslem religions are responsible for the modern world and all its technology, for they are heirs to a biblical faith that encourages a realistic and down-to-earth view of human beings and their environment. There is no science in the modern sense in the Bible, no experimental research into the workings of nature. But there is a new vision of reality, a vision that has made it possible for us to do such extraordinary things as to put men on the moon, conquer the scourge of smallpox or build the nuclear bomb.

The texts of scripture were written in an age when the world, for the majority of people, was ruled by ignorance, haunted by gods; powers to be propitiated and feared. Some even demanded human sacrifice. The Bible records a revolution in thinking and a new freedom for humanity's questing spirit. It was this liberation from ignorance that laid the foundations for the development of science. There is only one God, proclaimed the new insight. He is the creator of all things: people, made in his image, are his agents upon earth; they have authority and responsibility. His praises are sung beautifully in Psalm 104.

In the following chapters, I raise some of the issues we need to ponder and debate, if we are to take our God-given responsibilities seriously. A religious faith should embrace the knowledge that science reveals, for, at its best, it is concerned with truth and describing the way things are, in this extraordinary evolving universe. Science has done much, in particular, to clarify our view of who we are, where we have come from and where we might be going.

At one extreme of the debate will be those who believe that science has all the answers and has replaced religion. They deny God and take the view that the universe is nothing but matter, energy and a clutch of impersonal forces which (somewhat surrealistically) have purposelessly spun all the riches and beauty of nature. At the other extreme are the fundamentalists who, in the name of religion, reject many of the most exciting discoveries of science. Then there are those who get side tracked with religious fervour into areas which resemble science but are not: astrology and the pursuit of UFOs. We need to be alert, to think clearly, and to recognize rubbish when we see it.

Many of the issues that we need to ponder are practical. How are we to use the knowledge we have gained? Science hands us great power. Some believe that, in polluting the world through technology and exterminating many living species, we are fast laying waste to God's creation. Others take the more optimistic view that, used wisely, science can contribute to the building of paradise on earth.

We share with God the power to create the future – perhaps this is what it means to be made in his image. The question is, will we use our new skills in a God-like way?

I

From GUTs to TOEs:
No Need for God

An idea past its sell-by date

There's nothing new about the claim that there is no God. Chinese Confucian scholars, over two thousand years ago, took the view that religion, with belief in gods, spirits, ghosts and ancestors, was good for the common man and his family (holding society together, giving succour in times of crisis), but that the educated gentleman sees the childish nature of such beliefs. Even earlier, in India, the Buddha had dismissed belief in a divine Creator as unhelpful. And the Psalmist must have had someone in mind when he wrote, 'The fool has said in his heart, "there is no God".' Now a new voice speaks, saying that the idea of God is dead, that there is no God. It is a voice which carries great authority in our society: the voice of science.

Or, so some would have us believe. But we must, as usual, beware of sweeping generalizations, the language of tabloid newspaper headlines; particularly when they are misleading. The truth of the matter is that, while *some* scientists believe that their field of study leads them to conclude that God is an unnecessary hypothesis, one they can do without, there are others who find that science awakens within them deep religious feelings. Science does not speak with one voice. And while some scientists are brilliant within their own discipline of study, that does not guarantee that they are good philosophers. They can talk rubbish, and believe it, as well as the rest of us: but, perhaps, with more authority.

It began with GUTs: Grand Unified Theories. In the nineteenth century, electricity and magnetism were thought to be different phenomenon, until it was discovered that in reality they are different manifestations of the same thing, electromagnetism. The twentieth-century quest was to show that *all* the forces of nature (gravity, electromagnetism, and the strong and weak forces that hold atoms together and cause radiation) are all children of one original force produced at the moment of creation in the Big Bang. Tie into this theory the discovery that all matter (itself a 'solid' form of energy) is made up from two basic types of fundamental particle, quarks and leptons, and you have a set of equations which explain the universe. They could be written on a postcard, printed on a tee shirt. The Hebrew prophets of the biblical period would have *loved* it!

The radical belief that informs the whole of the Old Testament is that there is only one creative power behind nature and history: Yahweh, God of Heaven, who made both Sea and Dry Land. The carved and statuesque gods of the Egyptians, Babylonians, and Canaanites (some of them representing forces and powers of nature, sun, moon, stars, thunder storms and so forth), are all dismissed. Only God is God. It was the first Grand Unified Theory. This momentous insight generated three great religions, Judaism, Christianity and Islam. We are heirs to their vision.

New developments in science, discoveries in astronomy and the quest for a Grand Unified Theory (a tantalizing dream not yet realized), seemed to support this Hebrew vision. Overwhelming evidence from optical, radio and microwave telescopes strengthened the theory that the universe began with one dramatic act of creation, fifteen billion years ago, now known as the Big Bang. The Big Bang is hard to visualize, perhaps impossible: it is unlike anything else in our experience.

In the beginning, it is proposed, an unimaginably gigantic storm of energy roared out from a point source, from a seed, or 'singularity' in the language of maths. It blossomed from nothing, generating space and time, expanding and evolving, creating galaxies of stars and planets, and became the cosmos we observe today. It hurts the mind to try to make sense of such an event, puts a strain on the imagination. There was no time before creation happened and no space in which the explosion could take place; both these things emerged from the 'seed' with everything else. One cannot ask 'What was there before time began?' – the question makes no sense. (Stephen Hawking has likened this problem to asking what lies a mile north of the North Pole. From the North Pole one can only head south: from the beginning of time there is only one way to go – forward with the evolving universe.)

Cosmologists play with the maths of the first few minutes of this moment of creation, turning the mystery into elegant mathematical theory. Some dig deeper and attempt to describe the first trillionths of a second, known as the epoch of inflation, when the laws of physics and the nature of the evolving universe were determined.

The universe now observed by astronomers strongly confirms this scenario. The light from distant galaxies of suns, analysed by spectroscopes, is shifted to the red end of the spectrum, revealing that they are flying away from our own galaxy, the Milky Way, in which our own sun is one star amongst a hundred billion. The further away the galaxies, the greater this 'Red Shift', and the faster they recede from us. The bigger the telescopes and the further they are able to peer into space, the greater detail astronomers are able to add to this picture of an expanding universe. Trace this expansion back through time and we come to that explosive event, which began it all. Listen to the universe with microwave receivers and we can still 'hear' the 'afterglow' of the primaeval fireball.

The theory of the Big Bang is science's description of what people in the Western faiths had always believed, that the universe is a dramatic manifestation of one single act of creation. God said 'Let there be Light', and there was Light. The Hebrew prophets had been right in their insight that there is only one power behind creation. The laws of nature all tie together as though the result of one beautifully refined idea. The universe is rooted in a single unifying thought. Scientists were about to read the mind of God in the language of mathematics.

Then came the TOEs (Theories of Everything) and some theoreticians began to take their claims further. Not only could the universe be described in a single coherent set of mathematical equations, but these equations, they asserted, needed no further explanation. Everything there is to be said can be said by science. The cosmos needs no creator. Time and space, energy and matter, emerged out of nothing and needed nothing to get them started. Just as one has no need for the idea of God to explain why $2 + 2 = 4$, so the laws of nature make complete sense without reference to anything beyond themselves.

The universe, it is claimed by those who would do away with God, began as a 'quantum fluctuation in the void'. Just as matter can materialize 'out of nothing' in a field of energy, they argued, and then disappear again (a phenomenon well known at the quantum level of minute fundamental particles), so the universe materialized out of nowhere. It just happened to happen. There was nothing – and then out popped something. And here we are!

Martin Rees, one of the architects of the Big Bang theory, and Royal Society Research Professor at the University of Cambridge, has said of those atheist physicists, who would conjure the universe out of nothing, that 'they should watch their language'. 'Nothing' is a notoriously difficult concept. The 'nothing' between galaxies, permeated by energy fields, is a very different void from the imagined 'nothing' talked of by religious philosophers who speak of God creating 'out of nothing'. The 'nothing' of the physicist is seething with energy and not a true 'nothing' at all.

Thoughts of nothing have tantalized philosophers and storytellers for millennia. In Genesis, the world was a 'formless void' before God set about creating. In Teutonic mythology, in the beginning 'there yawned in space a vast and empty gulf' – they even gave this 'nothing' a name, Ginnunga Gap! Shastika Indians of California wove a tale about how everything was created from nothing by the Old Mole Id-i-dok, who heaved a giant molehill up out of the void thus creating the world. All of these poetic images try to cope with an impossible idea – that once there was nothing.

Children find it quite easy to appreciate the problem. The instruction 'For prep tonight, since we have been talking about creation stories – think about nothing' is usually greeted with laughter and some disbelief amongst pupils. Then they take the task seriously and a lively debate ensues in the following lesson.

'I tried to think of nothing – but then I always found myself thinking about something else!'

'I wrote the word NOTHING on a piece of paper and stared at it for twenty minutes!'

'I shut myself in my bedroom, turned off the light and fell asleep.'

'I emptied my mind so there was nothing there but blackness – but then I couldn't get rid of the blackness!'

'I *think* I thought of nothing for a brief moment, but then I caught myself thinking of myself thinking of nothing! How are you supposed to get rid of yourself thinking?'

One girl seemed to have really got the point when she admitted, 'I forgot to do the prep. Or perhaps I *did* do it, but I was so successful that there is nothing to remember!'

Even the physicist Stephen Hawking, who professes *not* to believe in God, is clear about the distinction between a complete mathematical description of the universe and the fact that there *is* a universe to be described. 'What is it that breathes fire into the equations?' he asks in *A Brief History of Time*. 'Why does the Universe go to all the bother of existing?' Theories of Everything can never account for why there is an 'Everything' to talk about.

And Theories of Everything will never be complete until they include an explanation for all the richness we find in nature. A theory which ties together all the basic laws of nature must also give an account of the extraordinary world which has emerged through them, a world which includes, among other things, the mind of the scientist who formulated the theory. They must explain Einstein just as well as they explain gravity. Mathematical equations which give an account of how the universe got started tell us nothing about why after fifteen billion years butterflies and buttercups appeared in it, or how the grey matter of human brains can come up with brilliant ideas and fall in love with beauty.

Questions to consider

1. How close can one come to thinking about nothing?

2. Which is easier to believe – that the universe has no explanation outside itself, or that its explanation is to be found in a divine creator?

3. Buddhism teaches a religious faith without God. Could the Western faiths survive without their belief in a Divine Creator? How would they change if they gave up belief in God?

4. If it is true that science can do without God, can people do without God?

5. Why do people invest so much authority in science, believing that it can provide all the answers?

6. Scientists, like Professor Paul Davies, author of *God and the New Physics*, believe that the elegance of the cosmic

laws recently discovered by science, and the remarkable way they seem to have been fine tuned to generate a universe in which life and then people evolve, provide overwhelming evidence that a creative mind is behind it all. The progress of science in its search for GUTS and TOES leads them to believe in God. Why is it that the same evidence leads *other* scientists to reject belief in God?

7. The need for an explanation for the universe is only one of many reasons why people believe in God. What other reasons are there? Which reasons carry most weight?

2

Blue Dot Lost in Space

'Like a blue glass Christmas tree decoration, hanging in empty space,' said astronaut Dave Scott, describing the Earth seen from the Moon. His time spent on the Sea of Rains, with Apollo 15, gave only brief moments to contemplate his home planet suspended in the darkness, above him, amongst the stars.

Planet Earth, one of the nine planets orbiting the sun: a small fragile world. It would take more than one and a quarter million planets the size of Earth to fill the volume occupied by the Sun. And yet the Sun, gigantic from where we stand, is in itself rather a small star, a Yellow Dwarf to be precise. It is one of the hundred thousand million suns that swarm together in the system known to us as the Milky Way.

The Milky Way, an almost unimaginably vast snow storm of stars (it takes light travelling at one hundred and eighty-six thousand miles per second a hundred thousand years to flash from one side of the galaxy to the other), is a mere smudge in the total cosmos. The universe, at a very minimum, contains at least one hundred thousand million galaxies – maybe ten times that number.

Where does that leave us? Modern cosmology has reduced our world to a tiny blue dot lost in space; and yet our small human lives barely even scratch the surface of this diminutive planet.

Science has made us feel small, insignificant, almost nothing. It all began, it could be argued, with that mediaeval canon Copernicus, who set the ball rolling by demonstrating, with mathematics, that it is the Earth that orbits the Sun, and not the other way round. We were displaced from the centre of the universe. Ironically this should not have been the bad news it appeared to be in some quarters of the church. In the mediaeval scheme of things, the universe was visualized as a diminishing series of nesting crystal spheres, one inside the other. The outer heavenly spheres of stars, planets, Sun and Moon were ruled by perfection. Only when a mediaeval space traveller descended to the inner lowest sphere, the Earth, would he be expected to find imperfection and things going wrong in a fallen world. Earth was 'the pits' in mediaeval cosmology; one only had to dig a little further down to reach the fires of hell. It should have come as good news that Earth was up there orbiting amongst the heavenly spheres! But that is not the way Copernicus' opponents saw it at the time.

With the Copernican revolution in ideas, we had lost our unique place in the cosmos, despite its being a fallen world. Galileo, a generation later, was able to demonstrate, using one of the first hand-held telescopes, that the Copernican theory is correct. The Sun was found to be far from perfect, its face marked with sunspots; the planet Venus showed phases like the Moon revealing how it orbits the Sun; and four moons were seen circling the planet Jupiter (now known as the Galilean moons), providing direct visual evidence that the Earth is not the centre of everything. Our world is just *one* of the planets in the solar system; nothing special.

As technology improved and telescopes got bigger, so the universe expanded in imagination, and planet Earth shrunk smaller and smaller. The stars were seen to be suns, many of them giants, thousands of times brighter than our own Sun; stars in their billions, each one controlling, perhaps, its own family of planets.

It is good to gaze at the night sky and contemplate these things. And it can be done very easily with no more help than provided by a monthly star map, from a daily paper. Take an autumn night, for example, away from the light pollution of a town. In the north-west, the constellation of Cygnus the Swan (sometimes called the Northern Cross) points down the ribbon of light called the Milky Way. The bright star in the tail of the Swan, Deneb, is a white supergiant. Compared to our Sun it blazes like a bonfire compared to a flickering candle. Light (which could whiz round the world eight times in one second) takes well over a thousand years to reach us from Deneb, which means that we do not see it *now* on our autumn evening; we see it as it was in the days of King Alfred.

Swing the eye across the sky to the south and one can peer even further back in time. A faint glow of light, high up in the constellation of Andromeda, can be found with a little patience. Victorian astronomers referred it to as nebula (a cloud); they believed it to be part of our Milky Way system. But it was not until the 1920s that this nebula, numbered M31 on star charts, was discovered to be another galaxy far beyond the boundaries of our own galaxy. That wisp of light, visible to the naked eye, is a neighbouring 'island universe' made up of two hundred thousand million suns, and the light has taken over two million years to get here. We see M31 as it was when our ancestors were emerging from other primates on the plains of East Africa.

In astronomical terms, the nebula in Andromeda is a very close neighbour in space and just one of hundreds of billions of such star systems. The shiver that runs through the stargazer is not necessarily because there is a chill in the autumn air!

Progress in science has left us scratching a living, like insignificant insects, on the surface of tiny world somewhere in the remote corner of a vast universe that knows nothing about us. Worse than that, with Darwin's theory of evolution by natural selection, we also seemed to lose our special status on the planet. Human beings are just one species of primate, a mere twig on one branch of a sprawling forest of life, which has spread in a thin layer across the world. Once more, we are nothing special.

Thoughts such as these have led Professor Stephen Hawking to conclude that 'Human life is just a chemical scum on the surface of a minor planet orbiting round a very average star in the outer suburbs of one among the million million galaxies in the observable universe.' Professor Peter Atkins, of Oxford, echoes this view: 'in a sense people are worthless, there's no point, no purpose in people. People are just things that happen to have emerged from slime.'

Is that, in truth, all we are?

But just as science speaks with different voices (it leads some to believe in God, others to deny that there is any divine purpose in creation), so there are different ways of reading what science teaches. Rather like using binoculars: hold them one way and everything is magnified and close; turn them the other way and everything shrinks. While some scientists take the view that the universe reduces us to nothing, others read a very different message from the same evidence.

Anthony Hewish, Professor of Radio Astronomy at Cambridge, interprets the facts relating to our size in the universe in a way that enhances our position and significance. Putting it quite simply, he states: 'Without this vastness we would not be here.'

To understand this point, we have to trace our ancestry back through time to the materials from which life and people are created. It is the great discovery of all the sciences that we live in a changing, evolving, world. If we are to think of God as creator then we can no longer imagine him to have created once in the past. We have to see him as creating a process, a process through which life evolves and develops through the laws of biology. Human beings, with their sophisticated minds that can appreciate beauty and think scientifically, are the most remarkable products of that process yet known to us.

But life depends upon a very complex chemistry. To build a human body, evolution needs hydrogen, oxygen, carbon, nitrogen, magnesium, potassium, calcium, iron, zinc and many other elements. The early universe contained none of these elements. When the Big Bang had cooled sufficiently there was nothing but vast clouds of hydrogen and helium. No life could have evolved then. All the more complex elements, needed for even the simplest life forms, had to be built up from hydrogen and helium and this is where stars come into our personal story.

Gravity pulled the spinning clouds of hydrogen and helium into dense blobs that then began to burn as suns. The pressure and temperature (hundreds of millions of degrees centigrade) at the heart of those first suns was sufficient to switch on processes of nuclear fusion. Atoms of hydrogen were 'welded' together to produce more helium, and helium atoms 'welded' to create heavier elements, carbon and oxygen, which contain more protons and neutrons in their nuclei, and more electrons in their 'shells'. Even heavier atoms were produced in the more massive stars until the ninety or so elements, so neatly described by chemists in the Periodic Table, had been created. (Our own Sun is one such solar furnace of nuclear energy, converting hydrogen to helium in its depths. In the process a certain amount of mass is lost – about four million tons per second – it being transformed into pure energy, the heat and light that keep planet Earth warm.)

This was the dream and quest of mediaeval alchemists; how to convert one element into another. Specifically, they wanted to find the secret magic whereby base metals could be turned into gold. They failed. They did not have the fiery furnaces, which only exist naturally in the heart of suns; so alchemy gave way to chemistry. And chemistry discovered the true alchemy of the universe.

Human bodies and brains, along with buttercups and butterflies, are built from atoms 'cooked' in massive stars. To be available for the process of evolution, this chemistry had to be released from those ancient suns. This happened in two ways. Roaring gales of particles, stellar hurricanes, rise from the turbulent surface of hot stars and fan out through inter-stellar space, spreading clouds of hydrogen, carbon, oxygen and other atoms throughout the galaxy. And then, sometimes, a really massive sun ends its life dramatically as a supernova, disintegrating in a blazing ball of energy, blasting trillions of tons of enriched chemistry in all directions. (The temperature is so great in a supernova that it fuses atoms together into gold and uranium and other heavy elements. All the gold on Earth was created in this way at least seven billion years ago. Without this vastness, there would be no gold wedding rings!)

After ten thousand million years the clouds of dust and gas of interstellar space were rich enough in new elements for life to begin. New generations of stars were born from these clouds, and planets formed with them. Our own solar system was created at this time, about four and a half billion years ago, built from atoms carried on cosmic winds and the dis-integrated remains of exploding suns.

It has been rightly said that we are built from star dust. Let the reader, old or young, examine her skin for a moment. Pinch it gently. All the atoms from which life builds skin have a long and exciting history, each of which could be traced back through the food we eat; to the earth in which the food grew; to the broken rocks from which the soil was made; to the mountains which were eroded; to the early days of the planet; to the darkness of interstellar space; and back to the stars. Many of these atoms will already have been recycled many times, through the living tissue of fish and flowers, dinosaurs, birds, and even people of past centuries. Nature discovered recycling long before the green movement thought of it.

'Without this vastness we would not be here.' Human beings are one of the most extraordinary things to emerge in creation since the Big Bang. But it takes a vast and ancient universe to create the conditions necessary for the birth of humanity. The laws of physics and chemistry and biology, discovered by modern science, are really a cosmic recipe for making people.

Questions to consider

1. On what grounds might we believe that the universe finds its fulfilment in the evolution of people? Is it an unjustifiably arrogant view?

2. How would you counter the assertion that human beings are really nothing in the scheme of things?

3. Science has done a lot to make us feel small. What has it done to enhance human dignity?

4. Human beings seem to be products of cosmic chemistry. Is there more to them than chemistry? If so, then what is the 'more' and where does it come from?

5. Suppose it was proved that there is no life anywhere else in the universe: how would we then think of our world?

6. Suppose it is found that the galaxy is teeming with planets that are home to intelligent life: how would that effect the way we view ourselves?

3

Designer World

It once seemed obvious to Christians that God had made the world; there was such evidence of design in nature. Theologians even referred to the Book of Nature, as though it were a companion volume to the Book of Scripture, the pair of them spelling out God's sovereignty over the world, his hand in its design. Who but a loving creator would have the forethought to give the polar bear a warm fur coat? Who designed the humming bird's bill so that it could probe trumpet-shaped blossoms for nectar? Who arranged it that, while insects need flowers for food, flowers need insects for pollination? Who fine-tuned the hearing of bats so that they fly unerringly in the dark, by echo-location, catching insects on the wing? And what about the woodpecker?

The design of a woodpecker is remarkable in its detail, a feat of intelligent and clever engineering. It has an extraordinarily long tongue coiled inside its head with which to probe deep holes for grubs, a tongue that is barbed and sticky at the tip making it easier to harpoon its prey. It has two toes facing forward, two pointing backward providing a good grip on a vertical tree; and a splayed tail that the bird presses against the trunk to keep it steady. The beak is fashioned like a chisel, ideal for digging into bark for insects, drilling holes for nests or drumming as part of its courtship display. The concentrated energy of a working woodpecker has to be seen to be appreciated. A healthy adult can beat its head against a branch up to fifteen times per second, the sound resonating throughout the woodland. Any other bird would die of headaches! But the woodpecker's bill is supported by a strengthened bone structure; and it has a padded brain.

Wherever you look, nature seems beautifully designed, creatures neatly crafted to their task and their environment. In the eighteenth century this general observation was reckoned to provide the best evidence for God. William Paley, one of the best-known theologians of his day, expressed the argument in what has become a famous image. He likened the world of nature to the inner workings of a watch. A watch is made up of springs and interlocking cogs, meticulously fashioned moving parts, keeping track of time. Examine a watch and there is no doubt that in its history there is a watchmaker. *Someone* must have designed and created the elaborate mechanism. So it is with the woodpecker, polar bear, and bat. God is the cosmic watchmaker who designed the world and everything in it.

It was not long before objections were raised to this line of argument. First the poets, perhaps with deeper feelings or sensitivities, were quick to point out that life is not always beautiful. Animals in their normal daily behaviour are horribly cruel to each other, tearing other species apart for food, preying on the young and the weak. Nature, in its very essence, is 'red in tooth and claw'. And under the heading of nature we must not forget viruses, bacteria, AIDS, cancers, famines, storms, earthquakes, floods and avalanches of mud. If the Book of Nature speaks of God, then of what God does it speak? Is God cruel – or indifferent? Or can one continue to believe in the goodness of God in the face of such universal pain and death?

The second objection came with new developments in biology. When Charles Darwin finally, after much hesitation, published his epoch-making book *On the Origin of Species through Natural Selection* in 1859, the idea of evolution had been around for well over a generation. What Darwin discovered was the *mechanism* of evolution, the way it worked. And it turned out to be very simple. It also seemed to do away, at one stroke, with William Paley's analogy of a watch, and the line of argument that design in nature proves the existence of an intelligent creator.

Just as people and plants grow from small seeds, so the whole of life on Earth can be traced back to simple beginnings, to single celled bacteria, three billion years ago. From bacteria upward, each generation of life produces abundant variety (variety we now attribute to random mutations in DNA and to the mixing of genes through sexual reproduction). Some of these variations are better suited to their environment than others and go on to be the parents of the next generation. Those best able to cope in difficult, challenging, circumstances survived to breed. (The 'survival of the fittest' in shorthand.) The rest die out without reproducing themselves.

The law of the survival of the fittest applies at all levels. Bears with thin coats that wandered north through the tundra would not live long. Their brothers and sisters with thicker coats survived to breed – and so in the course of time, over generations, through a process of 'descent with modification', the world got polar bears. God didn't design them with fur coats; nature did it through selection. And the woodpecker got its padded brain because birds without some padding would never have become woodpeckers. Generation by generation the padding improved and so more efficient woodpeckers evolved. Those not so fit for the work dropped out of the story. (The history of evolution is littered all along the way with the sad corpses of the unsuccessful.)

Darwin had discovered that nature designs itself through natural selection (Arthur Wallace, often forgotten, came to the same conclusion at the same time). It was an insight into the way God creates life on Earth. In writing *On the Origin of Species through Natural Selection* he believed himself to be contributing to our understanding of how God relates to his world, and saw his book as a scientific continuation of William Paley's theology. Instead of imagining God taking a personal creative interest in the details of the design of each creature, the peacock's tail, the rhino's tusk, the woodpecker's padded brain, Darwin proposed that the divine act of creation was brought about through the establishment of general laws. The Law of Natural Selection was one such law.

Some of Darwin's followers take an atheist view of evolution, dispensing with God altogether, arguing that the laws of nature have their own inner logic: no divine law-maker is needed to establish them. Professor Richard Dawkins, author of *The Selfish Gene* and other best selling books on biology, develops this belief quite aggressively. With Paley's watch analogy in mind, he has described nature as 'The Blind Watchmaker'. Nature has no plans or purposes, it proceeds blindly through natural selection. It is not an intelligent designer, and does not work towards a goal. Creatures change and develop, adapting to their surroundings, to the competition for food, to pressures from enemies and changing climate, just as a matter of course. No overseer is needed, no God.

We can see the process of evolutionary change taking place in the 'artificial' circumstances of selective breeding. Pigeon fanciers, livestock farmers, nurserymen, racehorse owners, champion dog enthusiasts; they all interfere, deliberately, with the way creatures propagate. By selecting the parents with the features they want to enhance, they manage to produce tumbling doves, leaner cattle, double flowers of unusual colour, faster horses and dogs with impossible coats. This is exactly what nature has done over the past three billion years, but with one major difference. It all happens blindly, according to the atheist, by chance.

Evolution could be said to be an 'iffy' process; not an easy thought to digest for those who believe in God. The variations and modifications that occur in any generation are the random products of mutation, caused by errors in the copying of DNA, the effects of radiation, or the mixing of genes in sexual reproduction. They are no more guided than are the numbers produced by the throwing of dice. The progeny that then survive to breed are selected for by the harsh circumstances of survival in a competitive world. (In the real world of nature the tumbler doves and dogs with impossible coats would have been losers.)

The conclusion some draw is that we are all here by chance. Does that disturb our religious beliefs? Or can we see a role for chance, and the random event, in acts of creation?

Those who believe in a creator, and accept Darwin's view that God designs the world using the general laws he has established, and the opportunities offered by chance, may want to claim even more. There has been a lot of thinking this century along the lines that the traditional image of a God sitting enthroned above creation is unhelpful. God is better imagined as the creative power that runs through creation, the life within the life. In establishing the laws of nature, God does not sit back and watch them, 'from above', cleverly weaving the web of life on Earth, unaided. He is there *within* the evolutionary process itself. Taking an analogy from the world of pigeon fanciers, livestock farmers, nurserymen, and so forth, God is the 'hidden selector' working with each generation, ensuring that nature produces all its rich variety from porpoises to people, without getting stuck in some meaningless mush of amoeba.

The discovery that we are part of an evolving world has had some interesting effects on the way we think about ourselves. Our lives and our ancestry are intimately linked to the rest of the animal kingdom. We are primates with well-developed brains; the cats and dogs we keep as pets are distant cousins; we share common features, like backbones, with fish and birds and dinosaurs because we have evolved from the same grandparents. We carry the marks of our animal ancestry in our sexual drives and the aggressions that lie buried deep in our natures. The Christian doctrine of Original Sin was a mediaeval pre-scientific attempt to explain why the world is in a mess and why we are prone to behave selfishly. But we are imperfect, according to the theory of evolution, not because we fell from grace in the Garden of Eden, but because we have not yet learnt to cope with our natures or accept the grace which is on offer.

One of the most remarkable things about evolution is that through trial and error and the opportunities offered by chance, molecules of DNA, which contain the information for growing people, have twisted dust from the surface of Earth into consciousness. In us the chemistry of the planet wakes up and begins to examine itself. Science and religious faith are beginning to reveal something of who we are. Perhaps we have along way to go. 'Man is by no means a finished product,' wrote the Russian mystic Nicholas Berdyaev. 'Man is only what God is planning, a projected design . . .'

However one contemplates nature, whether as an atheist or believing in God, there is something so incredible and marvellous about its workings, something so improbable in its extraordinary and wonderful richness, that it is hard not to be stunned with awe. We are each of us born into this great tide of life and have for a moment, if we are fortunate, the joy of seeing it as a sacred process, transcending our small, often privileged, lives.

Questions to consider

1. Consider whether such an uncertain thing as chance can have a role to play in a deliberate act of creation.

2. What role has chance played in your life? Has it been good or bad?

3. 'The world is charged with the grandeur of God. It will flame out, like shining from shook foil' begins 'God's Grandeur', Gerard Manley Hopkins' poem on nature. In what way can God's handiwork still be seen in nature, even when all its adaptive detail (the woodpecker's

padded brain, the polar bear's thick coat) is explained by natural selection?

4. The Argument from Design has fascinated Christian philosophers down the centuries. They have called it the 'teleological argument' (from the Greek, 'telos' meaning 'end' or 'purpose'), arguing that the world seems to have been designed with a deliberate purpose in mind. It has been one of the most popular methods for attempting to prove the existence of God. Why have believers spent so much time and energy trying to *prove* that God exists?

5. How might religious faith benefit from seeing the world in evolutionary terms?

6. What can we read from the Book of Nature about God's purposes or his character?

7. The word 'evolution' is heavily loaded with ideas of progress and came, not from Darwin, but from his contemporary, the social philosopher Herbert Spencer. (Darwin only used the word 'evolved' once in *The Origin of Species* – he preferred to write about 'descent with modification', a phrase which contains no implications of getting better or worse.) In what sense has life on Earth made progress, with the emergence through evolution of mammals, and from mammals, people?

8. Nineteenth-century fundamentalists, such as Philip Gosse, defending the view that God created the world less than six thousand years ago, argued that he created it to *look* old. What do we think of the view of God implied in this belief?

4

Apes in the Family Tree

It came as a shock to respectable Victorians to find they had apes in their family trees. It disgusted them to think that beneath the veneer of polite society all men in reality are beasts. Charles Darwin had no problem with this implication of his theory of evolution. It seemed to him quite normal that man should be able to trace his ancestry back to the animal kingdom. But he was cautious in spelling it out. He knew that the wrong sort of people, rabble-rousing atheists, would seize on the idea that man has monkey origins, and use it to strengthen their antagonism to the Anglican Establishment. His great supporter Thomas Huxley had no such reservations.

Thomas Huxley's *Man's Place in Nature* was a best seller, illustrating that not all Victorians were opposed to the new teachings of science. The frontispiece portrayed a line of skeletons from gibbon through gorilla to man. This image, and variations, has been reproduced many times, a sort of cartoon icon of man's evolution, our ancestral line standing in a queue as though at a bus stop. The hairy ape at the back of the queue, long armed and low browed, slowly straightens in each figure until he becomes the clean-shaven business man with a rolled umbrella, ready for a day in the city. A leading contemporary of Huxley, however, dismissed it as a 'grotesque procession'.

The theory of evolution had done for man what Copernicus and Galileo had done before, in the sixteenth and seventeenth centuries; hurt his dignity and made him feel less significant in the universe than he had previously supposed. Copernicus had demonstrated with mathematics, and later Galileo confirmed with his telescope, that the Sun is at the centre of the Solar System and not the Earth.

It had been fondly held, until that time, that despite man's fallen nature, he was, nevertheless, at the centre and heart of creation. The Copernican revolution began to marginalize him in the scheme of things. The Earth shrank in the mind's eye and became just one of the circling planets. Then, in the nineteenth century, man discovered to his dismay that he was merely one of the brute beasts. It was another body blow. An outrageous slander. It was all too much to bear.

The notion that apes could, in the process of time, slowly turn into people was strongly opposed. 'Transmutation' was vehemently rejected as a heresy. Man had been made in the image of God, according to scripture, and not in the image of an ape. We should remember, of course, that the claim that we are descended from the apes is an over simplification. We are not descended from modern monkeys, as many Victorian cartoons suggested. But modern day chimps, gorillas, orang-utangs and baboons are our closest cousins: we share with them the same, distant, primate grandparents.

Various attempts were made to protect the dignity and damaged image of the human being. Some people clung tenaciously to the belief that God created all species as they are; cats were made as cats, dogs as dogs, and people as people. Rather like a toymaker carving a set of animals, giraffes, elephants, monkeys, for a child's Noah's Ark, so God produced all creatures great and small, in one go. Some evolution does take place, they allowed, but only *within* a species (as with the selective breeding of exotic doves by pigeon fanciers, or of dogs to produce lithe whippets, short legged dachshunds or muscular alsatians all from one wild type – the wolf). But one species cannot, they confidently asserted, transmutate into another. Apes did not become people. Many fundamentalists, particularly in America, are still of this opinion today.

Another view proposed that evolution had indeed

generated all life on Earth by a process of slow change and natural selection, but that in the case of man a special act of creation had been involved. Alfred Russel Wallace, who discovered the role of natural selection at the same time as Darwin, defended man's special status in this way. God, he argued, had intervened in biological history to produce a new creature with a soul, thus setting man apart from his ancestors.

Two features in particular, Wallace believed, could not be accounted for by natural selection; man's intelligence and his larynx. A brain that could do higher mathematics and compose symphonies was far more complex than anything evolution could have come up with simply to cope with the pressures and needs of primitive tribal life. Similarly, the larynx, which had evolved for purposes of communication, had the extra gift of bestowing on its owner the ability to sing the most sublime arias from an opera. Evolution on its own would never have produced something so refined. Nature only selects those features which are needed for survival in a competitive world. The mathematician's brain and the opera singer's voice came directly from God.

Other Victorians, however, welcomed the discovery of our kinship with rest of the animal kingdom. Darwin, angered by the arrogance of those who put man on a pedestal, was secretly pleased to put him back in his place. And, having observed a young orang-utang having a tantrum, concluded that 'our descent is the root of our evil passions'. Man's selfish, fallen, nature had traditionally been accounted for in terms of his inheritance of Original Sin from Adam and Eve, who ate the forbidden fruit in the Garden of Eden. Evolution suggests that man never was perfect, and he carries in his genes the necessary selfishness needed to ensure survival in what is often experienced as a hostile world. Darwin even went so far as to suggest that 'The Devil, in the form of a baboon, is our grandfather.'

Huxley, developing the same view, encouraged optimism.

Man came from the apes, but is not *of* them. He is not de-graded by association with his ancestors – he has ascended above them. Our origins may be humble but our future is noble. This emphasis on progress appealed to those who had not been born with the special privileges of upper class Victorian society. Self-betterment had the backing of science: it had almost become a law of nature.

There are many people at the end of the twentieth century who still find our ape ancestry hard to stomach. A Gallop Poll conducted in the USA in 1991 revealed that no fewer than 46% of Americans believe that we were created within the last ten thousand years very much as we are. Their view of the world is dominated by a fundamentalist interpretation of scripture. Many others, however, seem to have come to terms with the idea that human beings share distant grandparents with all other members of the animal kingdom. (Trace our family tree back a billion years and we share grandparents with the wheat from which we bake our daily bread.) General education and the steady stream of wild life programmes on TV have accustomed us to seeing chimps greet each other with bared teeth and deferential gestures, so that we laugh with recognition the next time we watch the guests being intro-duced at a party. And we are no longer astonished to hear that 99% of the DNA of a chimp is the same as that in our own genes. It only takes a small 'one word' change in the DNA sequence to create a naked hairless ape; and another small change instructs the brain to go on growing for longer, there-by producing a potential mathematician or composer.

The distinction between human beings and other animals has become blurred. The ability to communicate with more than just barks or yelps was once thought to be the exclusive preserve of mankind and yet we now know that whales and dolphins communicate through song. Chimpanzees can go even further and master over a hundred symbols from which they can construct simple sentences. And the ability to make tools was thought to set us apart from all other creatures.

Now we can watch chimps on TV making sponges of moss to collect drinking water from deep holes in trees, or learning how to crack nuts with a stone. And some species of birds have been observed to select an appropriate stick as a tool for extracting insects from small holes. We are not as different as we thought.

'Do you have a problem with the thought that we are all animals?' I asked a class of twelve-year-olds. 'Not at all,' replied one pupil. 'I rather like the idea that my cat is a distant cousin!'

'Or, you could say,' suggested another, 'that the apes might have a bit of a problem with the way their descendants have turned out!'

Questions to consider

1. Why did some Victorians feel degraded by the discovery that we have apes in the family tree?

2. What is meant by the claim in Genesis that men and women are made in the image of God?

3. What is it that distinguishes us from other animals?

4. What lessons are to be learnt from the discovery that human beings are one branch of the mammal kingdom?

5. Richard Dawkins has calculated that if a twentieth-century human were to stand on the coast of Africa, hold hands with a parent, and they with *their* parent and so on back through history, by the time this human chain reached the heart of the Congo jungle the hand holders would be our ape ancestors. If you could review such a

parade how would you recognize when the apes became people?

6. If evolution is an on-going process, how might the human race evolve in the future?

5

Raven Guides Sailor to Land

Floki Vilgerdarson, one of the first Norsemen to land on the shores of Iceland, in AD 860, was given the nickname Hrafna (the Raven), because, the story goes, it was a raven that guided him to land. Mariners often kept these birds on board for that purpose. It was in days long before maps, compasses, and clocks made it easy to plot a voyage across the great ocean, or a Global Positioning System could give you a fix on your position to within a few metres. A pet raven, flying to-and-fro in the storm, was the best a sailor could hope for. Although Hrafna was the first settler, and gave Iceland its name, he only stayed two years.

Ravens regularly figure in the ancient legends of seafarers. In the Sumerian *Epic of Gilgamesh*, Utnapishtim, who survived a great flood by building a boat and filling it with family and animals, let loose a raven, with a swallow and a dove, to check whether, somewhere beyond the horizon, the waters had retreated. Noah likewise, in the biblical account of a flood, sent out a raven, 'which flew back and forth as it waited for the waters to dry up on earth'. It was then a dove that brought back positive news, in the form of an olive branch. Birds have a prominent role in these early sagas.

The ancient tale of Noah, embedded in the Hebrew text of the Book of Genesis, is one of the oldest and best-known stories of a great flood. So well known, and so much part of our cultural and religious heritage, that it has come to be remembered as *The* Great Flood. There is its nursery appeal, a part of toyland; the animals going into the ark, two by two, the elephant and the kangaroo. It must be, amongst children, one of the best known of all the Bible stories. But there is more to it than the charming image of a peaceful boatload of animals surviving a catastrophe, lions and lambs in neighbouring stalls, giraffes standing together sedately, tourist class. The terror induced by fast rising waters is known in almost all communities. Fear of flood lurks deep in our dreams.

The dark side of water is that it drowns people. And although floodwaters may rise slowly with heavy rain, giving a chance of escape, some of the most dramatic floods may happen in the twinkling of an eye. A tidal wave, a hundred feet high, triggered by a distant underwater earthquake, can sweep over a coastline and inland before anyone has time to gather their clothes or fold up their fishing nets. A storm surge in a cyclone may inundate hundreds of square miles of low-lying land, in hours, leaving people with no alternative but to climb trees or float with the flotsam. (A million died in such a tragedy in Bangladesh in 1990.) A river bursting its banks can pour down streets faster than a crowd can run.

Melt waters from mountain snow and retreating glaciers may form enormous temporary lakes held precariously in place by moraines of rock and earth. The bursting of such a natural dam sends a multi-million ton wall of water pounding down the valley to the sea; a roaring cataract of rock and flood destroying everything in its path. Nature demonstrated its power this way, many times, after the last Ice Age. As global warming shrank the ice caps (opening up new fertile lands for human settlement and cultivation), tremendous floods were frequent. Geologists can point to the evidence. One of the most dramatic episodes must have been when rising sea levels caused the Mediterranean to break through the Dardanelles, turning a low-lying fertile plain into what we now know as the Black Sea.

It is no wonder that the turbulent ocean forced its way into creation myth as a symbol of darkness, disorder and chaos, the deep that God conquers and controls. In the beginning, Genesis tells, the earth was a formless void and there was darkness over the deep, until God said 'Let there be light', separated the waters from the waters and made dry land appear. The fear of flood lies behind these potent images.

Almost every ancient culture has its flood story, some of them possibly dating back ten thousand years to the end of the last Ice Age and the beginnings of agriculture. Pygmies, Maoris, Aztecs, Inuit, Icelanders, Persians, Jews, and dozens of other peoples have sagas and myths that record a disastrous deluge, which in each case came close to wiping out their world. When this pandemic of tales was first discovered, fundamentalists took it to be evidence of one universal cataclysm, supporting their belief that the story of Noah truly records a world-wide flood that wiped out all life on earth saving those who were saved in Noah's ark.

Science's answer to this fundamentalist interpretation is quite straightforward. Firstly, there is no evidence of a flood swamping the whole world: there is ample evidence that major flooding has happened many times in many places. (There is even the particularly relevant evidence of a major inundation, covering an area the size of England, around the ancient city of Ur where Abraham came from, about six thousand years ago. This may have been the catastrophe remembered in the story of Noah. It seems to have been an area of great flooding, because the *Epic of Gilgamesh* contains a flood story very similar in form and detail to the story found in the Bible.) Secondly, there is not enough water on the planet to cause a world-wide flood. If all the water locked in the polar ice-caps, in glaciers and snow fields were to melt and all the moisture in the atmosphere were to precipitate as rain, sea levels would not rise as much as two hundred metres, leaving an awful lot of land untouched. (And if the water had mysteriously come from the heavens in the form of giant comets, then it would still be here.)

For comparatively small isolated communities, a major

flood would seem like the end of the world, and many record it as such in their flood stories. It makes complete sense that they should tell their stories in this way. The development of the skill of storytelling marked a major stage in the evolution of human society, every bit as important as the discovery of fire or the invention of the wheel. Those craftsmen who worked with words used the skill of storytelling to put great catastrophes into perspective, to find some meaning in the terrible tragedies that left their ancestors dumb with anguish, numb with loss.

There is an inner logic to the dozens of flood stories told around the world, an archetypal pattern that emerges through them. They share many features in common, not because they refer back to one great flood, but because they all arise from the same human response to disaster. Why did the flood happen? Why did the hero of the story (with family or friends) escape? How did they find land? What problems did the survivors face? How did the world get started again? Will there be a repeat of the tragedy?

The anger of a god figures in many of the sagas; aroused by mankind's disrespectful attitude in the Maori tale; because of the noise of too many people keeping the gods awake in the Babylonian epic; as punishment for wickedness in the story of Noah. The focus varies from story to story, depending on the culture. The Smith River Indians, of California, make much of the loss of fire (not a problem for Noah); the lone survivors, stranded on the top of a mountain, 'cook' their fish by holding them tight beneath their armpits: their descendants, Spider Indians and Snake Indians, fly to the Moon in a gossamer balloon and steal fire, which they bring back to Earth. The biblical story, on the other hand, is influenced by its Jewish origins: seven pairs of each of the clean, kosher, animals are taken on board, compared to only one pair each of the uneatable unclean animals. Different interests and concerns get worked into the same overall structure.

Sometimes the details are remarkable in their similarity; the release of birds to find dry land is a common feature. Ravens and doves have their role in a storyteller's search for meaning. But the major force behind most of the stories is the probing question, 'Why was there such a terrible flood?' It is a question we still ask today, when faced with natural disaster.

By asking the question, we reject (as did our ancestors) the fearful possibility that life has no meaning, that we live in a pointless world, an absurd and purposeless chemical accident in an uncaring universe. This is the real issue raised by the flood story recorded in Genesis. What happens to our faith in the love of God when nature unleashes its destructive power? Why does God create a world where people are suffocated indiscriminately by mudslides, crushed under their houses by earthquakes, drowned by storm surges?

Biblical fundamentalists reject this view of flood stories and use the story of Noah as evidence for a different scenario. Interpreting the creation story in the first chapter of Genesis as a literal historical account, they calculate that the world was created less than ten thousand years ago (and not 4.6 billion as claimed by modern geology). They would like this view taught in schools, calling it 'Creation Science', as an alternative to the theory of evolution and to the general body of science teaching. When geologists point to the overwhelming evidence for an ancient Earth, they have a simple answer. All the great mountain building, the laying down of coal seams and layered rock strata, the accumulation of snow in ancient ice caps, and the stranding of fossil fish and sea shells hundreds of miles from any ocean, are a consequence, they claim, of the turmoil caused by the biblical flood. They call their theory 'Catastrophism'. But 'Catastrophism', like 'Creation Science', disregards the knowledge carefully accumulated by many scientific disciplines over the past four hundred years. It is not *science* at all.

Jim Irwin, an astronaut who flew in Apollo 15 and walked on the Moon at Hadley Rille, adopted 'Creation Science' beliefs on returning to Earth, despite having been trained for

years by geologists to look for the 'Genesis Rock' (chunks of
the oldest material in the Solar System). He established the
High Flight Foundation and led expeditions to Mount Ararat
in Turkey to locate the remains of Noah's Ark. Satellite pic-
tures had revealed a boat shaped object on the flanks of
Ararat. When the feature turned out to be a rather strange
lava formation, this did not curb the enthusiasm of either
Irwin or his colleagues. They wanted to establish the truth of
a literal interpretation of Genesis and to deny the authority of
the very science that had put satellites into orbit and landed
Irwin himself on the Moon. All they found on one expedition
was a dead bird in the ice. 'Perhaps it was Noah's raven!'
remarked Irwin – presumably with tongue in cheek.

An interesting court case captured the attention of the
Australian press in 1997. A creation scientist, Dr Alan
Roberts, was touring Australia lecturing, promoting his belief
that Noah's Ark had been discovered on Mount Ararat
several years ago, and raising funds for a further expedition,
and to aid the growth of 'Creation Science'. A leading geolo-
gist at Melbourne University, Professor Ian Plimer, appealed
to the Federal Court to stop Roberts from disseminating his
views. Plimer was furious with what he considered to be 'fake
science', and felt strongly that Roberts was raising money,
illegally, by false pretences. The court dismissed the case on
the grounds that the creation scientists did not stand to gain
financially from their campaign. If people want to donate
money, to what others might consider a daft cause, then they
should be free to do so.

Questions to consider

1. How would we, at the end of the twentieth century,
   answer the question 'Why the flood?' (There are plenty of
   recent disasters to focus on.) Is a scientific answer (in

terms of changing weather conditions and so forth) sufficient?

2. What do we feel, today, about the claim made in Genesis that God was prepared destroy his world with a flood?

3. What lessons can be learned from the story of the flood in Genesis?

4. Should creation scientists be allowed to collect money to fund expeditions to locate the ark on Mount Ararat?

5. Can we see any divine purpose or plan in the terrible natural catastrophes that regularly afflict the world (earthquakes, floods, famines, etc.)?

6. Many Christian communities strongly defend their literal interpretation of the Genesis creation stories, and the story of the flood, denying the theory of evolution and all the evidence for an ancient universe, while believing that God created the world in six days less than ten thousand years ago. What is the appeal of this view?

6

The Case of the Disappearing Soul

'Body and Soul' was once a familiar way to refer to the complete human being. Now we are not so sure.

Part of the progress made by science has been to show us ourselves in the naked light of reality. We have learnt to focus on what we really are: members of the animal kingdom, built amazingly from chemistry. To make things clear to our understanding we often think in analogies and metaphors. One way that science has suggested we think of human beings is to see ourselves in mechanistic terms, as pieces of complex chemical machinery. 'Man is a machine,' it is asserted. But in the process we seem to have lost our eternal souls.

It used to be assumed, almost without question, that a human being is a duality, body and soul, made from two substances, the one physical, the other spiritual. When the philosopher Descartes, in the seventeenth century, began to look at man with the eyes of a scientist, he was happy to describe his limbs as levers and his heart as a pump; analogies taken from technology were both helpful and appropriate. But pumps and levers are predictable, as is the working of any piece of machinery. A dangerous slippery slope seemed to lie ahead. As science pursued its research and refined its descriptions, a person might be reduced to being no more than a bundle of mechanical parts. A robot. An automaton.

Descartes side-stepped this slippery slope and preserved man's spiritual dignity by keeping faith with the mediaeval belief that a soul inhabits the physical body, guiding and directing it. This, however, presented him with a problem.

How can a spiritual soul, free supposedly from the mechanistic laws of nature, influence a physical machine? His rather unsatisfactory answer was that the soul sits in the brain, like a pilot in his cockpit, directing the workings of his body through the pineal gland.

In this way Descartes safeguarded a human being's belief in the ability to make free moral choices: human behaviour guided by conscience rather than the predictable laws of science. It also meant that at death there was something of the person which could go on to another life: the door to heaven remained open.

In the twentieth century, our understanding of the brain and its relationship to the body has become more sophisticated. Removed from the head, the brain looks no more than a lump of soft grey matter, the size of a small Christmas pudding. Analysed, it is revealed to be made up from ten thousand million cells, with ten times that number of electrochemical connections, the knotted centre of the nervous system. It is the most complex piece of chemical architecture known on Earth. To understand it, another analogy from technology comes to hand. The human brain functions like a computer.

The brain's electrical circuitry is, of course, far more complex than any computer yet built or designed, but in principle it is the same, evolved by biology (rather than manufactured in the silicon chip factory), giving us an advantage over all other animals. But computers do not have souls and they can be switched off. And when switched off, they are nothing but cold, dead, hardware. So, too, it is tempting to infer, the human on-board computer functions while a person is alive, producing the conscious mind, and generating the illusion of a soul. But when we die, the mind, and belief in an inner soul, fade out of existence and nothing is left but inert chemistry: dust. There is no immortal soul, only grey matter.

Many people, today, are happy to take this view. They know where they stand. When you are dead, you are dead.

You will not be at your own funeral. No worries about what happens after death, because the answer is 'nothing'. No immortal soul survives death, nothing departs the body when you die. 'Soul', on this view, is just an adjective, a way of describing the deep inner feelings of a living functioning human being. It is not a thing in itself.

Others struggle to keep a different belief alive, clinging to the idea that there is a 'me' within the body; the 'real me', the 'ghost in the machine' which can talk about 'my body' as though it were a possession. Stories of out-of-body experiences reinforce this notion. Patients, from many cultures, who have recovered from near terminal comas, or survived temporary death on the operating table, often have remarkable tales to tell about floating above their bodies, watching from above.

At a cruder level, the pop culture addiction to ghost stories implies a belief in an inner being which can separate itself from the body at death, and flee the mortal shell.

Most of us, probably, oscillate between both views; we would like to believe in an immortal soul but are not always able to sustain the belief. As Milan Kundera reflects, in *The Unbearable Lightness of Being*, it is often only when we feel deep emotion that we return to the idea that there is more to us than just chemistry. In scientific terminology the nose may be no more than the nozzle of a hose sticking out of the body to take oxygen to the lungs; the face an instrument panel registering all the body mechanisms; the soul merely the grey matter of the brain in action. 'But just make someone who has fallen in love listen to his stomach rumble, and the unity of body and soul, that lyrical illusion of the age of science, instantly fades away.'

The difficulty for us, today, is that we are heirs both to scientific explanations and also to deeply ingrained religious beliefs.

Religions which teach reincarnation, that we have a series of lives, being born again and again, tend also to believe in the reality of an inner immortal soul (Buddhism is an exception). The *Bhagavad Gita*, the Hindu scripture written over two and a half thousand years ago, spells the belief out very clearly, in a discussion between the god Krishna and the warrior Arjuna, on the brink of a battle. (Arjuna has become worried that it is his caste duty to slay people. Krishna counsels him to think differently about death: it is not the end.) 'As a man leaves an old garment and puts on one that is new, the Spirit leaves his mortal body and then puts on one that is new' (II, 22). The body is no more than a transitory outer garment, something that grows old, wears thin and can be discarded. The real person, the soul, lives within, beyond the power of sword or fire, death or destruction.

Much of Greek philosophy entertained a similar thought: it assumed that the physical body, with all its problems, was a sort of tomb in which the soul was trapped. The goal of philosophy was the emancipation of the soul from the trials and tribulations of life.

The Christian tradition is the somewhat confused child of two rather different cultures. From the Greek world it took on board the idea of an inner immortal soul, that spiritual substance later championed by Descartes and generally assumed in popular folk religion: the soul which trails clouds of glory on entering this physical world through birth; the soul which goes to heaven at death, to the great comfort of those loved ones left behind.

From its Hebrew parent, Christianity inherited a different picture. Man is born from dust and at death returns to dust. 'Earth to earth, ashes to ashes, dust to dust' remains a powerful statement at the heart of the Christian funeral service. The life we have is the breath of God. Early Hebrews had no doctrine of life after death; God creates us for *this* world, they believed, and breaths life into us as he did into Adam. If we obey his commandments then we are blessed and live three score years and ten. After death our name survives, but no more. Later, as their theology evolved, they came to see a problem. Many innocent, good people die young, some in horrible circumstances. (They were particularly concerned about the young men who having fought for Yahweh in the wars of the Maccabees, were captured, tortured, and executed in front of their mothers.) Their belief in the faithful, loving kindness of God, and his justice, led them to believe that one day, in the future, these good people would be raised from the dead for their reward. Resurrection became the new possibility.

The Christian Nicene creed encapsulates this view: 'And we look for the resurrection of the dead, and the life of the world to come.' The suggestion is that we are physical beings, for whom death is death. No thought here of a ghost-like soul departing from the body to take up immediate residence in heaven. But we live with hope. God, we affirm, will keep faith with us and will raise us from the dead, somewhere, somewhen. (St Paul struggled with the 'how' of this, with his analogy of a seed having to die before the plant could grow, in his first letter to the Corinthians.)

The critical realism of science seems to have brought us back to our biblical roots. We are made from dust and will return to dust. We are complex chemical creatures produced by evolution in a material universe governed by God. But we are incarnations. Spiritual things are experienced by us in physical terms. The spiritual world is not some inner or parallel world to the material. The material universe is a manifestation of the spiritual. And, if God knows us and loves us, our immortality is guaranteed even before we die, because we already share in his eternal life.

Questions to consider

1. Read St Paul's First Letter to the Corinthians, chapter 15 and consider what it has to say about the nature of human beings and what happens after death.

2. What is distinctive about each person which might be identified with his or her soul?

3. Computers are becoming more and more sophisticated. One day their inner circuitry may match or even surpass the complexity of the human brain. Will they then wake up and know themselves, as we know ourselves? Will they speak of their souls?

4. How would life be with no hope of resurrection?

5. What do we lose by believing that people are merely chemical machines? Are we deluded biological robots?

6. Perform a thought experiment. We have already grown used to the idea that people can have heart and lung replacements: imagine it became possible to perform a brain transplant. Suppose a young couple, engaged to be married, are involved in a bad car accident; his body is irreparably damaged, but his brain is intact; her body is unscathed but her brain is beyond repair. Whisked to hospital, his brain is transferred to her body. Which family will claim the patient after recovery from the operation, his or hers? Would it make any difference to your conclusion if the brain was suffering from total amnesia?

7

The Myth of Free Will

Science is in danger of taking from us our free will – by telling us that we never really had it in the first place. We live with a lie, the illusion that we are free to make free moral choices, taking responsibility for our decisions and ourselves. In reality, we discover, we are no more than conscious, impotent, observers watching as we stumble from day to day, programmed like computers or robots to behave the way we do. The programming was built into us long before we had any control over the matter. Some of it was already with us when we were born, already printed into our nature genetically, baggage we inherit from our human and primate ancestors. Bits of this programming may even be reptilian, dating back hundreds of millions of years.

Then there are those early human experiences, which left their indelible imprints on our vulnerable new psyches. The way we were nurtured has a lot to do with who we are, whether we grew surrounded by love and security or were exposed to the unpredictable emotions of others, traumas, violence, deprivation or plain bad parenting.

The genetic programming of behaviour is very obvious in other creatures. Young garden warblers can find their way to East Africa, unguided, only weeks after hatching; barnacle geese fly from Greenland to enjoy Britain's mild wet winters, without being shown the route. The mystery of migration is still baffling – how a chemical code, strung out along the DNA molecule in a bird's genes, can transmit such information from one generation to another; or even how it manages to pass on the structure of a recognizable song without the grown bird ever having heard it from another of the same species. Weaver birds can build beautifully designed nests without instructions to follow, or examples to copy; spiders spin intricate and delicate webs for netting food. All of this behaviour, and much more, is encoded for in the creature's genes.

How much of *our* behaviour is dictated from within, is the big question? We may think we are free, while all the time we are running on predetermined railway lines like trains with no option but to follow the route laid down. It has even been suggested that heroic acts of human kindness, those altruistic actions when a person sacrifices his or her own life to save another, are part of our genetic make-up. Human genes have protected their future in a family or clan, by selecting the sort of altruistic behaviour which guarantees their survival, even if it is through somebody else. Dying for your country may be no more a moral gesture than is the spinning of a web by a spider, or than turning south over Iceland is for a barnacle goose.

Religious philosophers and, surprisingly, Christian theologians have sometimes contributed to this rather dismal view of human freedom. The reformer Calvin taught a doctrine of predestination to salvation, or to damnation. God had already decided who were to be among the elect, destined for heaven, long before anyone was born. The grace that leads to salvation, on this view, is an undeserved gift from God. The rest of humanity was condemned to follow the downward path to hell.

Other thinkers have built on their commitment to the belief that God is omniscient. God knows everything; nothing lies beyond his ken as he surveys his creation, there are no horizons to his knowledge. The future therefore is as visible to him as is the present and the past. It is we, who are stuck in a transitory mortal world, who cannot look beyond the present moment, making only vague predictions on what will happen next like people peering down a fog-bound road. God sits

above the world and the future is as real to him as the past. It
sounds very obvious and logical.

Time and human history on this view are sometimes compared to a book that has already been written. We human
beings are only able to read the story line by line, sequentially.
God, however, is able to open the book wherever he likes and
knows in detail what is to happen tomorrow, next year and on
the last page. A more recent way of stating this belief is to
compare history to a video. God can view the whole thing,
with action replays from the past – and from the future; but
we have to experience it from within, frame by frame. God
knows everything, so all our future actions have already been
decided and fixed long ago. Or have they?

Muslim philosophy has often developed this line of thinking. In popular belief, in some parts of the Muslim world, it is
held to be true that on the day you are born, certain things are
already fixed; whether it is your destiny to be rich or poor, if
you are to be a poet or not, and the date of your death.
Christian soldiers, in the First World War, were sustained by
a similar faith. 'If a bullet's got my name on it today, then
there's nothing I can do about it.' It can be a help, sometimes,
to resign oneself to fate.

But resigning oneself to fate as a permanent attitude to life
can cripple human growth. It saps at moral freedom, quietly
closes doors on unexpected opportunities, suffocates creative
decisions. We have to believe something different, if we are to
take moral charge of ourselves, exercise real free will.

In defence of the view that human history is a book which
has already been written, known to God but opaque to us, it
is proposed that we *still* have free will. But God knows what
decisions we are going to make before we make them, because
God knows everything. This may be true and many are happy
to leave the matter there, with no more questions asked.

Science's contribution to this debate has been to erode
further our faith in free will, by reducing all our decisions to
the influences of genes or upbringing. As washing machines

have been programmed to perform a variety of washes, so we have been programmed to behave in certain ways. Even belief in God has been reduced to tendencies arising from the neurophysical structure of the brain; the religion we then choose is determined by where we are born. Some people conclude that because anyone born in Ireland tends to become Roman Catholic, whilst children in Saudi Arabia become Muslim, that this provides sufficient grounds for judging that all religions must be wrong – because none can claim to be absolutely true. They ignore the possibility that the different traditions might share truths, or express deep truths in different ways.

Do we have genuine choice or are we deluded in thinking that we can make a free decision? Belief in free will must challenge the views that, firstly, the future is fixed, and secondly, that human decisions can be reduced to being the predestined outcome of a cluster of a genetic pressures and environmental influences.

As to the future being fixed, would it not be more realistic to suppose that the future does not exist in any sense, anywhere, not even in the mind of God, but only comes into existence when it happens? In that case God's omniscience will not include knowledge of future events, because they have not yet happened. In creating a universe for intelligent beings, God has taken a great risk. We only have to look around the world, consider human history, to see that this is the case. But God has the confidence (if we may use such a human term to describe him) that with love and time all will work out well. In giving us free will, he willingly limits his own power by sharing the god-like quality of being able to create. We are made in the image of God and he waits to see what we shall do with the opportunities that face us. We, in our freedom, like the stars and planets and all the laws of nature, are part of the way God expresses his will, creatively, from moment to moment and day to day. He does not read our history from afar, but is involved with us in its writing, in the unravelling of its plot;

creating the cosmic context, the material world and the laws of nature; sharing the pain.

The scientific view that reduces a human decision to being the predestined outcome of a cluster of genetic pressures and environmental influences must be challenged through an analysis of the experience of decision making itself.

The uniqueness of human self-awareness is its ability to transcend itself. There is no doubt that we each carry with us a heavy load of genetic baggage. Sometimes the load seems too hard to bear. Anger and lust can make fools of us. We are self protective, liable to crippling insecurities, prone to fears, blind to the needs of others. We may become addicted to tobacco, alcohol, drugs, or some sexual obsession. We make excuses for our behaviour: 'I was out of my mind,' 'I wasn't myself,' 'I was depressed; drunk; suffering a middle aged crisis . . .,' 'I had a difficult childhood.' But even if we do carry a lot of baggage, and feel that there is something inevitable about the course our life is following, we still have the power of free choice even if its exercise has become somewhat atrophied through disuse. We can transcend the pressures and influences, stand outside them and go a different way, maybe even use them to go in a different direction, in the way one steers a sailing boat. A sailing dingy is subject to sea currents and wind. The person on board can use these pressures to guide the boat to a safe haven.

One of our greatest capacities is to choose the attitude we take to our fortunes, however disastrous. Prisoners in concentration camps have born witness to the fact that there is one freedom the captors are never able to take from them, the freedom to adopt an attitude to their circumstances. If Nelson Mandela, twenty-seven years in a South African gaol, much of the time in solitary confinement, had dwelt on hate or revenge, he would not have emerged the man he was, emanating a power for calm, forgiveness and reconciliation.

Much of the time we programme ourselves. It is not only the unchosen dramas of early childhood that add shape to our characters. We play 'inner videos' of resentment or jealousy for example; replaying the anger and unhappiness, again and again, until they become part of our 'wired in hardware'. Then we behave badly, driven by feelings which, we tell ourselves, are beyond our control. But we have taken a hand in creating this person who behaves badly, and lost faith with our true humanity. We have let our minds and imaginations dwell on the wrong things. Destiny lies where the mind dwells. So we have no excuse.

Human freedom is not merely exercised in word and deed. We have a deeper level of choice in the way we think. It is in the *mind* that we grow in freedom or allow ourselves to become ensnared by emotional ignorance, greed or anger. This truth lies at the heart of Buddhism. It is reflected, too, in the phrase 'in thought, word and deed' found in the collects of the Book of Common Prayer.

It ought to be part of the Christian creed recited regularly. 'I believe that I *can* choose my actions and my attitudes. I take responsibility for myself.' And whoever recollects that his life is grounded in God will find that he is not alone in his attempt to transcend the genetic baggage he was born with, or which has shaped his experience. God will become in him, in the words of Jesus, 'a spring of fresh water, welling up for eternal life'. There is more help waiting within us than we often realize.

Questions to consider

1. Does the future exist in some sense so that God knows it? Does God's omniscience imply that he is able to foresee everything that is to happen, until the end of time?

2. What is the relationship between prophecy and future

events? Does prophecy depend upon the future already
having been written?

3. What do we feel about the suggestion that free will is an
   illusion? Are there times when we have experienced making a completely free choice, when we could have chosen
   otherwise? Do we often use our free will — or only rarely
   when faced with some dramatic moral challenge?

4. How free are the victims of bad parenting to become good
   parents?

5. Why does suffering turn some people bitter, while
   ennobling others?

8

Don't Just Pray About It – *Do* Something!

The news that someone, in his or her twenties, has decided to go into a monastery can spark off a surprising amount of anger. 'What a waste – why couldn't he do something useful with his life?' 'What does she want to spend her youth locked up with a load of nuns for?' 'Has he had a breakdown or something?' 'I never thought she'd opt out like this, it's weird – she must be scared of the real world.' 'If he wants to be religious why doesn't he become a social worker? He could help those street children (wherever it is they hang out) – at least do something *useful*.' And all along, there is a sort of restrained fury. How dare he, or she, scare us with the suggestion that sex, success and a money-making career are not important; that being alone in silence might be a good thing.

We live in a culture dominated by activity; restless with the anxious prejudice that our lives only have value and meaning when we are doing something. Even religion in the West has come to emphasize the social side of the gospel, supporting charities, helping neighbours, saving the environment. Which of course is good – just so long as it does not lead us to forget that there is an inner life, which needs time for growth, and that prayer is a positive, creative thing. (A Zen teacher, contemplating the West's obsession with activity, coined a neat aphorism; 'Don't just do something – sit there!')

The growth of science and technology has a lot to do with this shift away from an emphasis on prayer. Science will answer all mankind's needs. Medical research will find cures for AIDS, cancer and the common cold. Science will solve the food shortages in the Third World, developing new crops, controlling pests, and reclaiming wasteland. Technology will raise our standard of living. Science will bring home the daily bread, not prayer.

We have succumbed to a useless view of a helpless God. The development and success of the scientific worldview has taken away from God any creative role in human affairs. The creator has slowly been transformed into the Great Mathematician, the Cosmic Scientist who devised the laws of nature, generated the Big Bang and then sat back to watch the universe evolve without interfering from outside. He will not tinker with the mechanism, direct or redirect the process, or make changes to spare creatures pain. Every event is determined, and created in all its detail, by the laws revealed by modern science. The evolving world came to be seen as an enclosed world subject to law and order, a perfect mechanism with a lifetime guarantee; it needed no correction, oiling or repair.

The creator of this mechanical world, ruled by the laws of science, is the useless God described by the rational Deists of the eighteenth century; and he still lingers unquestioned in the minds of many believers and atheists. (It is *this* God which has led many people, in the twentieth century, to deny his existence and become atheist – quite understandably, because they feel no need for him.)

One consequence of such a view of God is a dwindling belief in the power of prayer. It contributed to the unthinking belief that people praying are merely mouthing words to themselves, wasting their energy, taking time out from the real world. It made it easy to reject the discipline of monastic communities dedicated to a life of prayer. What is the point of praying if it cannot change anything? Much better, surely, to get up off your knees and do something practical.

The absence of prayer left a vacuum. A spiritual emptiness.

Restlessness afflicted the soul and people turned to the East, to its teachings of meditation and contemplation, its images of saints and Buddhas sitting cross-legged in the lotus position, calm, at peace and in silence. 'What is prayer?' – 'Light sitting in light,' answered an Eastern sage. Obviously something was happening in the inner life which was worth knowing about, even if the Western part of the mind was repeating the mantra of science: 'You can't break the laws of nature; prayer won't change the world; only science can do that.'

Combining Eastern and Western traditions people began to taste the reality that can only be known through silence. Prayer became wordless illumination, the taste of 'knowing', contemplation, and the discovery of 'the still point of the turning world'. It needed no justification; it was its own delight. The joy of being able to give thanks in recollection of a good day, a helpful conversation, or a chance encounter was found to be good in its own right. So prayer became praise, contemplation, the inner welling up of gratitude, all enjoyed for their own loveliness.

For a time it did not seem to matter too much that prayer had been banned from interrupting the laws of nature and working miracles; that prayer could not alter the course of politics, feed the starving, or cure the cancer in a friend.

But then prayer began to flex its muscles again. Prayer changes the people who pray, it enables them to become more effective in their lives, more open to others, imaginative, forgiving and caring. And that changes the world around them. So prayer *can* change things, even in the belief system of those who still believed that the laws of science rule the world. But meantime, while prayer was being rediscovered in new ways in the West, something interesting was happening in science.

Science had moved on. Having redefined God, and made him useless in everyday life, science then made its own progress into new uncharted territories that have very different implications for the way God works that may relate to his world. We have left the 'Newtonian World View' (as it came to be called) behind. The Newtonian world was the world of nineteenth-century science, developed from Newton's Laws, which proposed that everything that happens is determined by mechanistic laws. The universe was likened to a giant billiard table: measure the mass and motion of all the moving particles and a 'super scientist' would be able to predict everything that happened next, until the end of time.

Such certainty has gone forever.

Two areas of research have contributed to this fundamental change: quantum mechanics and chaos theory. Now this presents us with a problem. The majority of us have little understanding of the physics or mathematics involved in either of these realms. And yet it is abundantly obvious, from the writings of those who do have a grasp of these branches of science, that they have significant implications for the way we think about creation. God's role in the affairs of the world will then have to be redefined. And the potentiality for practical prayer reassessed.

Quantum mechanics describes the world of fundamental particles, the quarks and leptons, protons, neutrons and electrons, atoms and molecules from which all larger things are constructed. Visualizing this realm is full of insuperable problems because the particles are not in any way like 'things' we can imagine. The complete prediction of the behaviour of an individual particle has been found to be impossible – and always will be impossible. (This Principle of Indeterminacy was made famous by the nuclear physicist Heisenberg.)

Chaos theory brings unpredictability in at another level. General patterns can be found in nature, in such systems as the weather, ocean currents, or turbulence in the flow of water in rivers or oil in pipes; but the beginnings of such patterns are lost in the minute detail of the initial conditions. Take an example from weather prediction. Feed into a computer all the facts necessary to predict next week's weather (millions of bits of information on changing temperatures, wind speeds, humidity, cloud cover, air pressure and so forth) and let the computer model of the weather system run, so that it tells you what will happen next. Bingo! Blue skies over Wimbledon!

Sometimes, however, the smallest alteration in the initial information becomes magnified with time and has such far-reaching effects that high wind, and rain, are the consequence (and we blame the weather forecasters). It makes detailed local weather prediction impossible for the long term. There are too many variables that may alter the whole developing system in an unpredictable way. (This has come to be known as the Butterfly Effect. The beat of a butterfly's wing in one continent may trigger a cascade of consequences that cause a storm on the far side of the world.)

Between them, quantum mechanics and chaos theory have loosened up science's control of the way we think about the world. Events are no longer imprisoned in a tight determinist grip. In many significant areas there is a new freedom for us to see things happening in an unpredictable way. The very process of thinking itself, for example, involving as it does the functioning of the neurones of the brain, is subject to quantum effects, and therefore indeterminacy. Major historical events may be swayed by the inclinations of an individual. Biological developments in the evolution of a species stem from minor shufflings in the genetic code of DNA. In all of these important areas there are innumerable alternatives where things may go one way or another; masses of opportunity for unpredictable outcomes. There is a central place in the laws of nature for total randomness. These 'moments of choice' give opportunity to God and to human beings to give direction to events. Prayer may do more than merely change people.

In the process of the evolution of life, in the unfolding of the tapestry of history, in the human events of everyday business and in the thinking processes of the brain, there are regularly *as a matter of course* times when things may go one way, or the other. At such points God may take a hand in their outcome, *without breaking any of the regular laws of nature*. His hands are not tied. He does not merely sit back and observe the laws of nature dictating their predictable paths; he uses the opportunities offered by the open-ended nature of the process of creation.

A personal recollection will illustrate this point. My father once told me that when he was a young actor on the stage in the West End, he was travelling through London by bus one hot summer's day. He was thirsty and, on a whim, got off the bus and went straight to a pub for a drink. There he bumped into a colleague who introduced him to a girl whom later he married: my mother. So I, my sister and three brothers and their families, my own four children, my grandchild Rose, and this book all owe their existence to that young actor's whim for a drink, on a hot summer's day sixty-five years ago. There is nothing special about this tale – every family has such stories, whether they get told or not.

All the events of history could probably be traced through such moments of randomness when things might equally have gone another way. Surely here lie the opportunities for God to interact regularly, every day, with his creation. Not interfering from the outside, not breaking any laws of nature, but guiding, nudging, responding to prayer, from within.

We can pray for healing in others with confidence that the activity of prayer may change things. We may pray for the world as monks and nuns do, from behind the walls of their monasteries, knowing that the structure of reality allows a place for effective prayer. We can pray for those around us, for family, friends and colleagues knowing that this is a practical way to practise loving.

The structure of reality is looser than science used to teach, more open-ended and amenable to being redirected. The New Science has made intercessory prayer possible again.

William Temple once observed that 'when I say my prayers, coincidences seem to happen; when I don't pray they don't happen'.

Faith and Science

Questions to consider

1. How much do we really expect to change the world by praying about it?

2. What part may prayer play in healing? Whose prayer?

3. Does prayer change things or does it only change people?

4. Is it a waste of time to pray (as in the Book of Common Prayer) for good weather?

5. Prayer has many purposes. What are they and which sorts of prayer are easiest to practise?

9

Whose Miracle?

There was anger in the school lunch queue.

'What *right* had he to say that?'

'He seemed to think God only cared for *him*!'

'It was the most unChristian thing I've ever heard!'

An ageing man, who had been a prisoner of war in Burma, had given the senior school lecture that morning. He had described the appalling conditions in the jungle where Japanese forces used prisoners, as a dispensable labour force, to build a railway. A film had been made of it, *Bridge over the River Kwai*. Death was a daily occurrence.

'Some of us were Christians,' he had said, 'and we kept our spirits up by standing together in small groups to pray. We had to be careful because the guards forbade us from holding meetings.' It sounded wonderful so far. Girls hung on his words. Here was a man for whom faith had made a great difference – maybe even saved his life. God was with him in the prison camp.

It was what he said next that aroused a ground swell of anger. The prisoners had prayed, in their small groups, that God would save them from death from malaria, malnutrition or exhaustion. They prayed they would be sent home safe and sound to their loved ones. They asked God for a miracle.

And God answered their prayers. The Americans dropped an atomic bomb on Hiroshima, killing one hundred and fifty thousand citizens at eight o'clock one morning, and sending a cascade of cancers down the decades. And then they dropped another on Nagasaki. The war came to an end.

'You'll hear people say that the atomic bomb was an evil thing,' he said, 'but for us in the prison camps it was God's answer to our prayers. Don't take away from us our miracle.'

Questions at the end of the lecture were restrained and polite. It was in the lunch queue that the anger surfaced.

By the afternoon the mood became more philosophical. Perhaps from his point of view the explosion of the atomic bomb had been a miracle. But could a miracle be so destructive and cause so much pain to others? It was then that someone remembered the Old Testament.

'What was the greatest miracle in the Old Testament?' asked a Jewish pupil rhetorically. 'Surely, the Plagues of Egypt and the crossing of the Red Sea when God drowned all those Egyptians. The Israelites thought it was a great miracle then, and we still remember it now, every Passover. Yahweh was fighting on our side, killing the enemy. That's what prisoners of war in Burma were praying for – for God to be on their side and protect them. I think we should let the man have his miracle.'

The word 'miracle' stems from Latin; *miraculum* – 'object of wonder'. Anything marvellous or extraordinary, any piece of good fortune sent by God, or the gods, could be called a wonder. In biblical times there was little understanding of how the world worked, and the 'laws of nature' imposed no restriction on God's activity. (St Augustine sagely commented that 'miracles are contrary to what we *know* of nature'.) God could do what he wanted; it was his world and he broke no laws to demonstrate his power. He could send a famine or a plague; hurl killing hailstones at an enemy, or raise the dead; brew a storm, let loose a flood or send seasonal rain. The power of God was part of the picture and it was expected that, from time to time, he would do something dramatic. No one believed that his power might be limited.

Miracles happened at every turn, for religious minded

people, and not only in Christianity. Earthquakes marked the birth of the Buddha, his enlightenment released showers of rose petals from the heavens; and Bodhidharma, founder of Zen in China, crossed the Yangste River on a reed. Even today, Hindu gurus conjure holy ash and bread from the air, and Muslims believe, from their reading of the Qur'an, that Jesus spoke almost as soon as he had been born (to defend the reputation of his virgin mother).

It was with the development of rational, scientific, thinking that miracles began to present a problem for faith. God had given us intelligence and the desire to find out how his world worked, it was believed, and science began to uncover the laws that govern nature. God was a rational being and had constructed a world that was dependent on regularity and order. The mathematics and the logic of these laws were seen to be beautiful. It became less and less likely that, having designed a beautifully working system, God would interfere with it, interrupting the regularity and order. And so God became the helpless God we discussed in relation to prayer; the God who devised the world like some elaborate computer programme and then sat back to watch, from his distant throne, the way the programme developed.

The effect on religious faith was to make people look more critically, and sceptically, at miracle stories. (Non-believers, of course, rather boringly dismissed all such tales as part of the mumbo-jumbo accepted blindly by the gullible.) The eighteenth-century atheist philosopher David Hume became, for many people perhaps unconsciously, a rational guide in the matter. We have learnt, through the eyes of science, to respect the laws of nature for their consistency and regularity; it is through the predictability of events that we come to understand the world and control it. Any report of an event that appears to break a law of nature may have another, more probable, explanation: witnesses misinterpreted the evidence, were misled, deluded, or plain mistaken. It is more probable that they got the story wrong, argued Hume, than that a law of nature, upon which we have learnt to depend for its consistency, has been broken.

While some people held tight to a view of the literal truth of scripture (if it is written that God made the Sun stand still over the Vale of Aijalon and killed the enemies of the Israelites with hailstones, then that is exactly what happened), others began to read some of the tales of miracles as symbolic stories, concerned with spiritual truth.

How many of the stories relating to Passover (the plagues in Egypt, death of the first born, Red Sea crossing, bread from heaven in the desert, and guidance on the road to the Promised Land) actually happen like that, and how much have they been enhanced in the telling, moulded by faith? The whole cycle serves an obvious educational purpose; to teach each new generation about what God has done for his people, and to inspire faith. But the true miracle behind the story is the regeneration of an afflicted, down-trodden people. Moses, inspired by God, led the people to greatness and the rediscovery of their identity. As a consequence the Israelites became the vehicle for new insights into the nature of God and his relationship to his creation. The Bible and later Christianity grew from this tradition.

Miracles in the New Testament could be divided quite easily into two groups, by Christians adopting a scientific view of the world: those that appeared to break the laws of nature and those concerned with healing. The nature miracles tended to be explained (not explained away) as symbolic stories. Images of Jesus walking on the water or stilling the storm express and enhance faith in his power to calm the turbulent world we live in, or overcome anxiety and stress with peace. The scenes are often used as imaginative exercises for contemplation. Feeding the five thousand and turning wine into water become symbols of the messianic banquet, the scriptural image for heaven. His gospel prepared his followers to celebrate the Kingdom of Heaven, which, he proclaimed, was already close at hand.

The healing miracles were easier for the rational sceptical mind to handle. Although some of these may be symbolic in their meaning (giving sight to the blind has obvious religious connotations) many of them must be rooted in real historical events. Human beings are both physical and spiritual. It has become a truism even in some circles of modern medicine that a patient has to be treated as a whole person. What goes on in the psyche effects the functioning of the body. The word psychosomatic, 'mind-body', has become part of everyday speech. So it is easy, even for a sceptic, to believe that Jesus had healing powers. He exercised them through love, forgiveness and the way he accepted, non-judgmentally, any one who came to him; and through the confidence he inspired in the sick or those marginalized by society. People turned to him, in the way they go to Lourdes today, or seek laying on of hands by a modern healer. Miracles happen. Patients are cured.

The more important question, however, concerns to what extent can a rationalist science-trained Christian expect miracles today and tomorrow? It is all very well to sort out what might, or might not, have happened in the past, and when one should read scripture symbolically rather than literally, but a lively faith wants to know about how God relates to the world *now*. Do the laws of science prohibit miracles on the grounds that it is through natural law that God designs and governs his world?

We have come across this issue before, several times. We wanted to know whether God, working within the process of evolution, has any room or opportunity for directing it; we explored the possibility of human beings being able to exercise genuine free will; and we asked whether prayer changes the world or merely changes the people who pray. The answer in all cases is that new developments in science have loosened up our image of the world. The laws of nature do not in themselves dictate everything that happens. There are many moments that hang in the balance. They may go either way;

there may even be *several* possible outcomes.

One may compare such critical moments to a father strik-
ing a ball in a family game of French cricket. In a fit of enthusiasm he may take a wild swing, smash a neighbour's window
and cause no end of problems; he may lob a catch to his
youngest daughter, to give her pleasure; he may let the ball hit
his leg to bring the game to a quick conclusion (because he
wants to catch the six o'clock news); or he may carelessly
drive the ball straight into his wife's eye and spend the evening
in the outpatients' wing of the local hospital. One moment
with several possible outcomes.

It is the nature of choice in matters of free will that we have
some power in selecting *which* outcome materializes in the
next moment. No laws of nature are broken. The way the
balance tips depends either on chance or choice. People, therefore, can purposefully influence events.

In the same way God can use the opportunities offered by
such critical moments to direct the world. Sometimes this
divine activity will appear as a miracle. Moses leads his
people, against all odds, to their Promised Land: Jesus heals
the psyches of the sick and health flows through their bodies.

This religious tradition authorizes us to live our lives trusting in the providence of God, expecting the unexpected, and
to have the strong faith that whatever befalls us all will be
well.

The word miracle has a spectrum of meanings, from the
totally unexpected occurrence which seems to have been sent
from God and runs contrary to the laws of nature, to the
simple astonishment felt when seeing the tiny fingers of a new
born baby. But they all share the common feature of wonder,
and in this sense we may even speak of the miracles of modern
science.

Questions to consider

1. The miracle of Jesus turning water into wine may be understood symbolically by a rationalist believer. But what of his virgin birth or the stories of his physical resurrection at Easter?

2. Can we think of any miracles that were contrary to the laws of nature?

3. Is it possible that, what is believed to be a God-given miracle from one person's point of view, is the cause of suffering for another? Can a miracle ever cause hurt and harm to someone else?

4. What miracles have happened in the twentieth century?

5. What characteristics does an event have to have for it to be called a miracle?

6. What part does the miraculous have to play in modern medicine?

7. When does it make sense to talk about the miracles of the natural world?

8. If God can work miracles, why doesn't he perform more of them?

9. 'For every event believed to be miraculous there must also be a rational explanation, otherwise we loose our free will.' Do you agree?

10

Pills or Sorrow?

Can I give you something?

'Suppose something tragic happened to a close friend, and you were very upset,' I put it to some teenage pupils, ' and you were offered the choice, either to take a magic pill which would immediately make you happy again, or to suffer sorrow, which would you choose?'

'Sorrow,' they chorused, without hesitation.

'It wouldn't be *right* to be happy,' added one.

'And whatever the pill did for you, it wouldn't be real happiness, anyway,' said another.

'Then suppose,' I continued, 'there could be a pill which made you happy *all* the time, whatever the circumstances – how would that be?'

They shook their heads.

'It would get boring.'

'There'd be no point in doing anything.'

'We need to learn how to handle sadness and sorrow.'

And finally one added as an afterthought, 'I *like* being sad sometimes.'

It can be very hard being a human being, particularly when one's emotions are in a mess, and people have drowned their sorrows in alcohol ever since fermentation was discovered. Drugs are not new; they have been around for thousands of years and used for medical, religious and recreational purposes in almost all societies. People have been smoking, chewing and drinking their way into states of comfortable numbness, or awakening their minds to new modes of consciousness, ever since they stumbled upon the strange and powerful properties of plants.

Religions have been ambivalent about the use of drugs, embracing them for their strange psychological effects or condemning them outright. Shamans and their followers have used them for heightened religious experiences, opening windows of the mind or creating vivid flights of fancy in the world of the imagination. In the Indian Vedic tradition the drug soma was used as a sacred stimulus to vision. Buddhists, on the other hand, reject drugs because they cloud the mind and inhibit true self-possession (though the Zen Buddhist ceremony of Chado uses tea-drinking as part of the ritual because it produces wakefulness!) And Muslims are uncompromising in their rejection of alcohol, much to the irritation of many unsympathetic Western travellers. (But, then, the Taliban fundamentalists of Afghanistan support the poppy harvest of the 'Golden Crescent', and facilitate the flood of heroin on to the streets of Britain to pay for their guns.) Christianity, meanwhile, has found little problem with the use of alcohol as a sacrament in the eucharist; and Jesus is said to have produced a great quantity of the very best wine for a wedding feast at Cana in Galilee. The moral lead we get from religion is a bit of a push-me-pull-you.

Today we live in a society swamped with drugs. The majority of people have come to take it to be a right and a norm to manipulate one's feelings through the use of caffeine, nicotine, alcohol or pills from the chemist. Some go further and use illegal drugs for recreational purposes, part of a lifestyle of emotional joy riding. It is big business.

Beer advertisements command prime time on TV. Tobacco companies spend millions on promoting sport in an effort to associate cigarettes with health, and in donating money to universities to buy respectability. They even hand out free fags at university discos to hook a new generation of clients (loosing three hundred customers a day in the UK through smoking-related death is an expensive business – they need to

replace their punters). And the profits to be made, by pharma-
ceutical companies for their shareholders, from tranquillizers
such as Valium or Librium (the latter once promoted by a
film of a lion co-existing peacefully with a lamb) and anti-
depressants, such as Prozac, are enormous. Prozac the
'wonder drug' is hyped to be 'bottled sunshine'; happiness in
a pill. One could come to believe from the literature that it is
the answer to all of society's problems.

Science has taken over from the amateur herbalists. Knowledge of our physical nature, our chemical make-up, is growing day by day. We understand the roots of physical pain and
can, most of the time, suppress it. We are mapping the brain
and analysing its chemical messengers, uncovering the role of
serotonin that is believed to regulate emotional behaviour. We
can target anxiety, insomnia and stress with tranquillizers
(preferring that term to 'sedatives') and we can relieve long-
term depression with the appropriate anti-depressant. Science
has introduced an era of chemical miracles. Or has it?

Drugs work miracles for some. But, for others, the pills
prescribed by the doctor may lead to a life of dependence and
addiction as effectively as alcohol, and the side effects are
not hazard free. What helps today may cause a deeper harm
further down the road tomorrow.

And if they are able to change the personality permanently
does that mean, when it comes to it, that we are no more than
chemical robots? If clever dispensing can turn a melancholic
person into a sociable jolly person are we left with any free
will? It is an unnerving thought that a pill can change my attitude to the world and influence my behaviour. And when
people use mood-altering drugs for recreational purposes
what are they saying about themselves?

It has been said that depression is the mental disease of our
time. It has been estimated to cost the American economy 43.7
billion dollars annually. Six million Americans are on the drug
Prozac (and also a fair number of pets apparently). Research
suggests that Americans born after 1955 are three times as

likely as their grandparent's generation to suffer from depression. And before we get complacent on this side of the Atlantic, we should note that the trend seems to be global. This raises some interesting questions. Is the world changing so that people really *are* more depressed – or are we using language differently, including in the definition of depression the experience of being moderately miserable? (Unhappiness is a natural part of the human condition and perhaps has an important place in the spectrum of emotions.) Or has the very existence of anti-depressants, like Prozac, created a problem and heightened expectations? We seem to live in an age where happiness is taken to be a right. Does that mean *all* the time?

This increase in depression may be symptomatic of the crisis of meaning and spiritual vacuum that marks the lives of so many people at the end of the millennium. The lack of a systematic and sure faith is leaving many stranded. Human beings are not merely chemical machines; they have souls and deep spiritual longings – even many atheists admit to this. The spirit needs guidance and structure. A spiritually purposeless life can be masked by hard work or partying, but there comes a time when the emptiness begins to break through the surface.

Ellie Wurtzel, writing of her own depression in *Prozac Nation*, reveals what a hard demon it can be to shake off. The emptiness she faced had no meaning to offer and depression would wash over her like a black wave. Yet in a strange way she came to love it and wouldn't let it go, because she believed it was all she had. Others have talked about wearing their depression like a heavy overcoat, one that they cannot remove. There is no question that in such cases Prozac can work wonders.

We each of us seem to be on our own in the matter of drugs, potions, and pills. We have to decide for ourselves, almost day by day, what to take and what not to take. It becomes in itself an exercise in mindfulness and self-possession, a challenge to the way that we cope with life's difficulties, to how we face grief or shoulder despair. How much alcohol can we handle? Can we give it up with ease, say in Lent? When does a reasonable recreational use of drink or the occasional 'pick-me-up' tip over into unhealthy dependence? How often do we use painkillers and what for – only for the severest headaches or more often than that to mask feelings of tiredness or mild hangovers? Do we use pills just to keep us going, when a rest or a radical change might be the better solution?

Some people go so far as to reject them all; caffeine, nicotine, alcohol, aspirin, tranquillizers, anti-depressants – the lot, on the purist grounds that they all of them interfere with our chemistry, and alter our natural state artificially. Others of us seek some sort of compromise, feeling grateful that we can control intolerable pain, while wishing, perhaps, that we didn't feel the need to take pills quite so often.

Questions to consider

1. What place does suffering have to play in life?

2. According to the Gospel of Mark, Jesus on being crucified was offered wine mixed with myrrh to drink – presumably to deaden the pain. He refused it. Does this detail from the crucifixion story have anything to say to us about our use of drugs; when they are, or are not, appropriate?

3. What role do drugs have to play in the treatment of grief?

4. Drugs can enhance the performance of an athlete. If the athlete is a cyclist and the drug is designed by a chemist to streamline the body's ability to pump oxygen to the muscles, is that any different from the application of the science of aerodynamics to the streamlining of his bike?

5. To what extent can one person really understand another's depression?

6. Define happiness.

7. How might we set about finding out whether someone's depression is a chemical or a spiritual problem? Or one's own?

Scientists Play God

Dolly had a little lamb

Dolly had a little lamb,
  Its fleece was white as snow,
And every where that Dolly went
  The lamb was sure to go.

Scientists are often accused, by the press, of playing God. When, in 1997, researchers at the Roslin Institute near Edinburgh succeeded in cloning a sheep, naming her Dolly, the accusation was made once more. A year later Dolly gave birth by natural means to a lamb, Bonnie; a gentle white-fleeced creature, who posed inquisitively for the world's media. Dolly and her little lamb will go down in history more surely than will the old nursery rhyme of Mary.

It had been a dream of science-fiction writers: and then suddenly it became reality. Scientists, keeping their research secret for fear of competitors, had managed the impossible, and astonished the world with the news. They had created a new creature by growing it from the nucleus of an adult body cell rather than by normal sexual reproduction. Dolly was an exact replica of her mother, a copy grown from a cell taken from her mother's udder. She was presented for photo-calls, a well-groomed, fat, healthy-looking sheep. A year later she produced her own healthy offspring. It was a marvel.

But then undercurrents of unease began to tug at con-sciences, as people considered the implications of what had been done. There were the scientific problems (not yet resolved at the time of writing). How would Dolly, cloned from a six-year-old ewe, age? The ageing process of cells is not entirely understood; would the cells in a clone age at the same rate as the parent? If so, then Dolly's body cells started life with a six-year-old handicap. And should we be talking of a 'parent' at all, or of an elder twin?

Deeper ethical issues became more worrying. If a sheep can be cloned, then why not other mammals – such as humans? Horrifying images from Huxley's *Brave New World* were conjured up: a world in which ranks of clones, identical laboratory-created people, live in a state of drug-manipulated contentment. Multiple copies pursuing identical lives: a mechanical science-created caste system, like an ant hill. And if that is all a bit far fetched, other possibilities are much more realistic. Suppose a childless millionaire, wanting to make a copy of himself or herself, to inherit the family fortune say, had access to a friendly laboratory. Should the law allow such a thing to happen? And if the law were to permit it, would it be ethical?

Even more extraordinary scenarios were dreamed up. Would it be possible to resurrect characters from the past? The great box office success *Jurassic Park* fantasized about the notion that it might be feasible to extract a thread of dinosaur DNA from the gut of a blood-sucking insect fossilized and preserved in amber. Thereby dinosaurs once more would stalk the Earth.

Access to a tiny blood sample, flake of skin, or lick of saliva on an envelope could provide the necessary chemical information to recreate the living or the dead. Someone could steal a bit of your DNA and, without your knowledge make a copy of you. Children could make clones of their parents and bring them up as their own children. ('I'll show them how to do it properly!') Neolithic man might walk again; or a pharaoh be grown from DNA extracted from his mummy.

One film producer has even intimated making an epic in which a clone of Jesus is made from a blood sample taken from the Shroud of Turin (supposing that the shroud is a genuine relic and not an ancient though mysterious work of art). We would then only need a clone of Hitler to have the ultimate movie, 'Christ meets Antichrist', or just simply 'Armageddon'!

Fact or fiction? We cannot even begin to contemplate the moral or theological issues here, until we have sorted out the difference between reality and fantasy.

Cloning would be a very expensive, risky and, at the present state of the art, difficult way of creating a baby. One wonders why anyone would bother, when the normal method of producing families can be followed with very little training, expertise or money!

It has to be remembered that cloning is, in a sense, merely an extension of a natural process. The DNA used by the scientists (who are accused of playing God) is not created by them but evolved over three billion years of evolution. That remarkable thread-like molecule, twisted into a double helix, is a chain of chemical instructions containing all the information necessary for growing a living creature, whether it be plant, insect, fish, fowl or mammal. In the case of the human mammal it contains the instructions for growing a nervous system and brain so complex that it wakens into self awareness, and is capable of writing poetry, composing a violin sonata or designing a nuclear bomb. Scientists use what evolution has handed down to them. By grafting the nucleus from an adult body cell into an ovum they can then grow a replica of the cell donor in the womb of a host parent. Nine months later a baby is born with all the physical features of its 'parent': in reality a 'twin', even though years younger.

Scientists, in what has to be acknowledged is a very clever bit of technology, have simply replicated a natural process whereby two people can be grown from the same set of information. In the case of identical twins, where the process happens naturally, it is the result of the spontaneous division of the original ovum. With a clone, the information is gathered at a later date so one has the oddity (maybe ethically unacceptable) of twins whose age may be separated by a generation. For doing this the scientists may be accused of playing God; in reality, they could counter, they are merely manipulating what God has given them through evolution. A more complex version of taking, and growing, a cutting from a plant.

The really important issue which leads many astray, and about which many fanciful fictional assumptions are made, has to do with the nature of human individuality; that separate 'soulness' by which each of us is a unique creation with a unique history. DNA is in danger of being overrated. Human beings are more than their genes and cannot be defined merely in terms of their DNA.

Human DNA, remarkable though it is, is no more than a chemical recipe for growing a person. The details are left to chance and circumstance. In the case of identical twins, for example, their fingerprints grow differently. (DNA does not need to encode this sort of detail, and it would be cumbersome to do so.) Even more significantly, the way a baby grows into a person is subject to all sorts of factors; whether the child is talked to, loved and cared for, or neglected, abused and made to be fearful of life, numb to feelings of empathy or compassion. We each of us have a personal history which contributes to who we are. We grow by grace, by the attitudes we adopt and the decisions we make. Much depends on the society we are born into and the company we keep.

Realize this and we begin to see that we are responsible for those around us and the way they grow into people. And this is not just a matter of good parenting: friends, people we work with but may not like, younger siblings; even our own parents! We have the power to damage our parents, stunt their continued growth; we also can play a part in liberating them to live lives of secure happiness. The truth is, we grow each other.

A clone of Jesus (heaven forbid that someone should try) would not *be* Jesus, but a twentieth-century child of Jewish descent, in need of love and care. A clone of Hitler would take on the culture of the family who fostered him: he would not be Hitler. The multi-millionaire who wanted to perpetuate himself by cloning from a body cell, would face, a few years later, all the familiar delights and problems of having a teenager in the house, with a strong family likeness, but struggling, quite naturally, to assert his own unique independence.

Questions to consider

1. What are the ethical issues involved in deciding whether it would be proper to clone a human being? Could it ever be right? If so, in what circumstances might it be acceptable?

2. How much responsibility should we bear for the way people around us grow?

3. What are the implications of any answers that arise from the previous question, for the way society treats prisoners who have been jailed for anti-social behaviour? Does the media have a responsibility not to demonize the worst offenders?

4. What of the suggestion that we should make clones of the best members of our society?

5. Who should decide whether a person should be allowed to make a clone of himself? The courts? The government? The doctors involved? The person himself?

6. Another area in which scientists are sometimes accused of playing God is in the practice of xenotransplantation – the surgical transplantation of organs from animals into people. We have become accustomed to the success of

heart and lung transplantation: but patients on waiting lists are still at the mercy of fate and dependent on donors being raced into hospital from fatal road accidents (instilling a macabre sort of hope at the best). It is now realistically proposed that human hearts be replaced by pigs' hearts, ones that have been grown for the purpose. There is a risk (we don't know how great) that a pig's virus could get into the human system this way, flourish and lead to a nightmarish pandemic. Apart from this danger, are there any ethical issues arising from the plan to give ailing patients the hearts from pigs?

12

Frankenstein Plants and New Super-Weeds

It's not natural

'I happen to believe that this kind of genetic modification (when genetic material from one species of plant, bacteria, virus, animal or fish is inserted into another species) takes mankind into realms that belong to God, and to God alone,' wrote the Prince of Wales, in the *Daily Telegraph*.

Prince Charles, a great supporter of traditional agriculture, decided years ago to farm his own land organically, that is without the use of artificial pesticides or fertilizers. In his newspaper article he voiced the views of a great many people who believe that we have every right to feel scared of genetically modified (GM) crops. Frightened because we don't know the implications; the science of genetic modification is moving so fast that there has been no time to think. What are the health concerns and how are they assessed – and by whom? Already GM soya is mixed with ordinary soya and is an ingredient in many foodstuffs we eat daily, such as chocolate or cakes.

There are a number of deep-seated worries. The genes of oilseed rape and sugar beet, for example, have been modified by the insertion of a gene taken from bacteria, which protects them from the effects of weedkiller. It sounds ideal. It means that the farmer can spray the crop and kill everything except that crop. But this leaves the field sterile for all other forms of wild life. The weeds are gone and with them the insects and then the birds. In another example, a gene taken from a snowdrop and inserted into a potato made the potato resistant to greenfly; it also killed the ladybirds feeding on the greenfly. This may be tidy, and economically efficient, in the short term, but a nightmare for the countryside in the long term.

Then there are all the unforeseen consequences. Potatoes, genetically altered to make them resistant to blight and viral infection, have been found to affect the immune systems of rats. And there is evidence already that modified genes of oilseed rape can spread beyond the field of the new super-crop. Cross-pollination with wild relatives of the GM crop will create super-weeds resistant to the weedkiller. Once the genie is out of the bottle it can never be put back again. GM is irreversible and there may be hidden dangers.

Other fears focus on the control big business has on our lives and the environment, through the creation of powerful monopolies. When the high-tech agricultural company that creates and sells the genetically modified seed is the same company that sells the weedkiller to which the crop has been designed to be resistant, then it will have gained total and unhealthy control of the market.

It is quite understandable that the average non-scientific citizen begins to fear that big business interests are creating Frankenstein plants and super-weeds that will grow beyond our control; that the world is being hijacked by multinational companies whose only concern is immediate financial profit.

'It's not natural,' one hears.

And it all feels thoroughly unnatural as we read the hyped headlines about the latest experiment; glow-worm genes inserted into tobacco plants to make them emit a warning glow when they need water, or tomatoes that have a new gene to make them frost resistant or a redder colour.

But what *is* natural? We all know what it means – until we come to think about it. The word conjures up images of the world as it is supposed to be, the way God made it before thoughtless people interfered with its God-given order. It harks back to an imagined era of static perfection – perhaps the Garden of Eden – ignoring the fact that life on this planet is dynamic, moving, evolving, always marked by change. This nostalgic understanding of the word ignores, too, that human beings, for all their faults, are part of, and a major expression of, nature. It is as natural for us to use our sophisticated brains for developing science and technology as it is for a blackbird to build a nest.

What can be more beautiful or natural than a classical English garden? And yet very little in it can really be called natural, apart perhaps from the occasional weed. (And how pleasing it can be to find the odd nettle in a neighbour's well-ordered flowerbed!) The neatly mown daisy-free lawn; the clipped hedges; the rich abundance of the herbaceous border, all of the blooms cultivated and created by generations of gardeners; luscious lupins and gigantic chrysanthemums. The whole glorious scene sings of man's interference with nature. Even the so-called 'wild garden', sown from a packet on pre-prepared ground, is richer by far than it would be if the plot had been left to its own devises.

Jean-Jacques Rousseau wrote to an American gardening niece, in the eighteenth century, instructing her to have nothing to do with double primroses, on the grounds that God had never intended them to be like that. Such purist reservations are rare. The Chelsea Flower Show, which could on Rousseau's principles be billed as a Celebration of the Un-natural, is nevertheless immensely popular. While one might consider a new, strangely coloured, rose as a bit 'over the top', the general feeling is that gardeners, through selective breeding and grafting, have done a good job in developing and exploring the potential of flowering plants. They bring out the best in nature, guiding its evolution, making it blossom in new ways.

Nor is the countryside any more 'natural' than the English garden. Our agriculture has transformed the surface of the world. The classical English landscape would be smothered in forest, scrub and swamp if it were not for human activity.

Consider the old hedgerow that borders a field or overhangs a country lane; its rich variety of oak, ash and alder; its briars and dog roses, old man's beard and birds' nests. There are no hedgerows in the wild; they were all planted by somebody to bring order to the land, creating fields, separating farm tracks from the crops, and controlling cattle.

Difficulties with the concept of what is natural do nothing, however, to allay fears and concerns about the genetic modification of crops. When we start to introduce snippets of gene from one species into another, are we going too far?

Defenders of GM argue that there is nothing to fear from genetic modification for this is how evolution has worked on Earth for the past three billion years. It is in its essence a natural process. If there had been no genetic modification 'in the wild' (albeit blind and random) then life on Earth would have progressed no further than the level of bacteria. We are all of us genetically modified versions of our ancestors. If the modification of genes had stopped, somehow, sixty million years ago then mammals would have remained as small shrew-like furry creatures; there would be no cats, dogs, elephants, whales, mice or men. We owe our lives to random processes of GM; we have evolved by natural selection, the survival of the fittest. The modifications that conferred some advantage on our ancestors survived into the next generation.

The same principle is true when one examines the history of agriculture. Human beings began to cultivate the land about ten thousand years ago, as the world emerged from the last Ice Age. When farmers first harvested and winnowed their wheat, oats and barley, they collected and saved the best grain for the following year. Generations of selection slowly improved the quality of the corn so that today it is very different from its wild ancestor. By interfering with nature we speeded up the natural, but blind, process of evolution in a direction that suited ourselves. And the next time we turn a fat and juicy corncob in the butter on the plate we might reflect that the unmodified wild ancestor of maize grew cobs that were no more than half an inch long. Domestication by artificial selection has increased the length of the cob thirty-fold.

Whatever our fears that scientists in the pay of big business are creating Frankenstein plants, it is very clear that humanity has been interfering with nature for a very long time. The big question is how far should we go and what are the implications for the future? They may be more far reaching than we are able to predict. Who could have imagined that twenty-four rabbits taken to Australia in 1859 would have four hundred million descendants by 1995, costing the Australian economy billions of dollars? Any change we make to the world will have some unpredictable consequences, and we should remember that scientists themselves are unable to foresee all the consequences of their experiments. There is no such thing as a risk-free life.

Prince Charles, in his rejection of GM crops, appealed for more choice and for a wide public debate on the matter. We need to be well informed. Foodstuffs should be labelled clearly so that shoppers may decide for themselves whether or not they want to consume genetically modified products.

Genetic engineers may now have at their fingertips skills that will unlock miracles and help to feed the growing population of the world. At the same time they may unwittingly trigger irreversible chains of events leading to disaster. Who should decide whether a particular modification to a crop should be allowed? Do we let the forces of the market place, driven by big business and the desire to make profits for the shareholders, make the decision? Do we hand responsibility to the scientists performing the experiments? Is it enough to have products marked so that we at least know what we are eating?

Questions to consider

1. Is it possible to produce a satisfactory definition of the word 'natural' that includes the activities of human beings? How would it be worded?

2. Eco-warriors have been hitting the headlines recently with their campaign against genetically modified crops, tearing up fields of plants at night. Do they have any justice on their side?

3. How should society decide what risks to take in the alteration and improvement of food?

4. Genetic engineering is not limited to the modification of genes in food crops. The process is as easily applied to animals and to humans. What view are we to take of reports that alterations could easily be made to chimps, who share 99% of our genes? A small snippet of DNA known as a regulatory gene controls the growth of a specific part of the body. Humans have larger larynxes than chimps. Transfer the gene that controls the larynx from a human to a chimp embryo and you could then train the chimp to talk. Would that be immoral?

5. Genetic engineers now talk of the possibility of modifying a fertilized human egg to correct an inherited disease by eliminating the defective gene. This 'germ-line' engineering could go further, adding genes or changing some, to create designer babies – smarter, stronger, faster or more resistant to disease. This way humanity would begin to take control of its own evolution. Does the Christian belief that we are made in the image of God have any bearing on this issue? What does 'made in the image of God' mean? Does the image have anything to do with genetic chemistry?

13

Extinctions: Who Next?

When William the conqueror was invading Britain, enormous birds were stalking the grasslands and forest fringes of New Zealand. The flightless Moa, twelve feet high and weighing half a ton, was a gentle herbivore with simple needs. It had a small dog-sized head, a long neck and a massive body containing an efficient gizzard full of large pebbles, the mill for grinding the leaves and twigs that were its diet. It had no enemies. But then came Maori settlers, and the Moa was easy meat. Very soon they had all been hunted to death, demonstrating that not all extinctions in the modern era are due to the ruthlessness of Western civilization. One of the great wonders of the bird-world had been consigned to irreversible oblivion. All we are left with are some artist's impressions and a few bones. Never again will the giant Moa roam the land, quietly plucking leaves from the trees. Never ever.

Extinction is a troublesome word. It scares us. It might be our turn next. Normally, when an animal or plant dies there are more where that came from. The red-backed shrike is no longer a breeding bird in this country, due in part to the loss of hedgerows and the use of pesticides; but there are still plenty of this species of shrike in India. When a species becomes extinct, however, it has reached the end of the line: for ever. Time is a one way street and there is no turning back.

Many people on hearing the word 'extinction' think, probably, of dinosaurs or dodos and, strangely enough, may suspect that their dying out was somehow their own fault.

The Dodo, flightless like the Moa, but smaller (about the

size of a large turkey), lived on the island of Mauritius, and was eaten by the Portuguese. It became extinct in the seventeenth century because it was so easy to catch. The Dodo was too trusting. Silly bird.

And cartoonists still conjure up the image of the Dinosaur as a sluggish dim-witted monster, to represent anything that has become slow, lumbering and doomed to the scrap heap of history; the inflexible politician of yesterday, or a tired old socialist regime out of touch with the times. The Dinosaur, like the Dodo, deserved to die.

But this goes against all the evidence, and is exceedingly unfair to dinosaurs. They were an adaptable and immensely successful species, efficient in their various designs, ruling the planet for over a hundred and twenty million years. (The human race, in comparison, had only been around for a hundred thousand years: a mere fledgling.) The dinosaurs finally died out, sixty-five million years ago, when their doom was sealed by the impact of a giant meteorite from space. Modern technology, in its pursuit of oil, has found the remains of the one hundred and eighty kilometre crater, deeply buried in the Yucatan peninsular in Central America. It took a flying mountain ten miles high, travelling at forty kilometres a second to wipe the dinosaurs from the face of the Earth. Hardly their fault.

Slowly, we are beginning to wake up. The floodgates have opened. Extinctions are a way of life on Earth. Darwin recognized this truth over a century ago when his travels through South America revealed to him the vast number of species that had been consigned to oblivion. Evolution is not a comfortable tale of a steady progress, a happy ascent from amoeba to man; it has another thread, a sad lament woven into the story. This threnody tells of the great global catastrophes that punctuate the saga. The immense obliterations of the past are a shocking and regular feature of the planet's history.

There have been a dozen major extinction events over the past billion years, resulting in so great a loss of life-forms that the planet is now populated by less than 1% of all the species that have inhabited the Earth successfully in the past. The most famous extinction (and most popular in the annals of science) brought the Cretaceous era to an end sixty-five million years ago. The K/T (Cretaceous/Tertiary) boundary is marked, world-wide, in the rock strata, by a narrow band of mud stone, containing tell-tale amounts of iridium, evidence of the meteorite impact which brought death to some 70% of species, including the dinosaurs.

An even greater extinction happened two hundred and fifty million years ago, signalling the end of the Palaeozoic (ancient life) era. It, too, may have been brought about by the impact of a colossal meteorite, or a comet. There is some evidence of a vast undersea crater off the coast of the Falkland Islands which may mark the epicentre of the gigantic 'million H-bomb' explosion, which wiped out 95% of animal species, including the giant reptiles. Dinosaurs then took over the world, as did the mammals after the later dinosaur extinction.

Each extinction cleared the ground, as it were, for a new development in evolution. It could be argued that had it not been for the meteorite that wiped out the dinosaurs, or the catastrophe that devastated the giant reptiles, we would not be here. We owe our lives to mega-death.

Researchers have looked for a pattern. With some stretching of the imagination the dozen or so major extinctions can be shoe-horned into a twenty-six million year cycle. Is this evidence of some astronomical rhythm, a distant mini-star, perhaps, orbiting the Sun and periodically disrupting sleeping comets from the Oort cloud, and hurling them into the heart of the solar System? It is possible, but not proven.

Other culprits are suspected. Severe climatic change, triggered by solar activity or a spate of volcanic eruptions, causing sea levels to rise or fall dramatically, could be enough to interfere with food chains and destroy habitats on a global level. Or, violently disintegrating stars (supernovae) in our local region of the Milky Way Galaxy could account for sudden world-wide disasters. Any such cosmic explosion within fifty light years of the Solar System would flood the world with such a shower of radiation as to cause immense harm to the biosystem and irreparable damage to innumerable species.

The first clearly recorded great extinction afflicted a watery world of bacteria and algae, six hundred and fifty million years ago at the beginning of the Precambrian era. And the last? We may, unwittingly, be living through the heart of it, even now. The question is, will we survive?

The eruption of mankind across the face of the Earth, in the past eleven thousand years since the retreat of the last ice cap, has transformed the planet. Our impact on other living species may turn out, in retrospect, to be every bit as devastating as anything wreaked by asteroids, comets, or climatic swings triggered by Sun or volcano. But then there may be no one around to think retrospectively.

At first it was the hunting. The Maoris in wiping out the Moa were not the only tribal people to hunt a species to death. North American Indians are sometimes idolized romantically for the way they lived hand in glove with nature, preserving the balance, respecting the earth. (The Buffalo Dance was performed to ensure that they kept a sustainable relationship with the animal they needed, the dance 'guaranteeing' that the number hunted was equalled by the number bred each season.) The fact is, the Native Americans exterminated many of the great mammals of the Americas in their pursuit of food. They plundered nature as thoughtlessly, and just as thoroughly, as any modern multinational business clearing rain forests for quick economic gain.

Sometimes, of course, the extermination was deliberate. Settlers in the USA killed off the grey wolf because it began to prey on the farmers' live stock (inevitable since the same farmers had already destroyed its natural supply of food). The buffalo of the prairies was hunted, almost to extinction, in order to starve out the tribes who depended on it for a livelihood. The golden eagle disappeared from England because of the (exaggerated) threat it posed to lambs: a shilling reward was paid for each shot carcass.

Then it was the land clearance. The hacking down of forests began thousands of years ago with the first settled farmers. Now, with a fast expanding world population, farming has become big business. We all depend upon its success; our supermarkets and fast food outlets overflow with its products. But we are the lucky ones: much of the world still lives near levels of starvation. The consequence is that, as we try to extract more food from the ground, we turn to science and technology to make our methods more efficient. Herbicides, pesticides and genetically engineered crops lead to more productive fields. Insects, weeds and mice vanish; birds, lacking food, disappear. So, in the reasonable interest of efficiency and profit, we tidy the world to death.

Only recently has the rate of extinctions become a matter of popular concern. Science, which has increased our control and dominance of the world, tidying it up in the interests of efficiency, has also revealed to us many truths. We begin to love creatures, ironically, just as they are about to disappear; animals we once took for granted as permanent features of nature. We have discovered that whales sing and communicate with each other over hundreds of miles, and see them as sentient animals in need of saving, rather than as convenient sources of blubber. We begin to appreciate the ferocious beauty of the tiger and realize that it is being fast driven to oblivion by poaching and the diminishing areas of its forest habitat. The American national emblem, the bald eagle, has been hit indirectly by pesticides, reducing the number of breeding pairs perilously close to the limit for a sustainable population. The list of species close to extinction, because of man's activity, is too long to print.

But all is not lost. We know what is happening. Science, which has helped us to destroy, has also given us the means and the ability to preserve. Whale watching has become a great tourist attraction; the grey wolf has been reintroduced (not without opposition) to the Yellowstone Park; golden eagles breed again in the Lake District; the bald eagle, a conservation success, has been removed from the Endangered Species Register. The Royal Botanical Gardens at Kew is building up its Millennium Seed Bank to store safely the DNA of endangered plants. The list of projects, reflecting our increasing efforts to save endangered species, is also a long one.

But the big question we have to answer is about where we stop. What do we preserve? Everything?

Life on Earth, we have discovered, is a developing, changing thing. Extinctions have played a natural and creative part in building up the rich world around us. They may be sad, but they are a natural part of the process; they may even be necessary. We might be wrong to turn the world into an unchanging zoo. We might be right to let some species go. Stopping the process, interrupting the flow, could be rather like stopping a piece of music at your favourite bit: it would make little sense.

Questions to consider

1. How do we decide which species to preserve?

2. Can we conceive what the world would be like if mankind were one of the species to suffer from the current epidemic of extinctions? Does the Christian belief in the ultimate triumph of God's purposes in creation rule out the possibility that the human race will become extinct?

3. Why would it matter if people disappeared from the planet?

4. Explain the urge that makes us want to save the whales.

5. What might be the consequences that follow from living with a global policy dominated by economics, rather than by principles of conservation?

6. What moral principles should underlie our thinking about the danger humanity poses for other species?

14

Leave the Moon Alone!

'Why don't they leave the Moon alone?' complained a pupil when we were discussing NASA's recent discovery of water in deep craters at the lunar poles. (The *Lunar Prospector* had picked up the neutron signature of thinly spread deposits of ice in the lunar soil, the crystallized relics of ancient comets.) Other pupils echoed the sentiment, sounding, perhaps, a bit like those of their more reactionary great-grandparents who, appalled at the invention of aeroplanes, protested, 'If God had intended us to fly he would have given us wings!'

It may be that my protesting pupils are right. Is the invasion of a neighbouring world, one in its nature not designed for human habitation, an improper thing to do? Do we really want to have our satellite exploited by big business?

The gentle Moon, so loved by poets and gazed at by lovers, has hung peacefully above the traumas and heart aches of this world since long before man first stood upright and started to contemplate his life. Sailing the skies, beyond the sound of war or revolution, the Moon has always provided an image of calm, a haven of peace. Now science and technology is set to conquer it. And with conquest comes pollution.

Images of a lunar landscape littered with obsolete machinery, discarded space junk, mining equipment and spoil heaps come to mind: the wasteland of the industrial revolution spreading out from Earth like a plague. There has even been the horrifying suggestion that the face of the Moon could be sold as advertising space; the logo of a well-known soft drink projected by laser at peak viewing times!

In the two Genesis stories of creation, mankind is given power over the fish of the sea, the birds of the air and all wild beasts; he is even given the responsibility of naming them. Created in the image of God, men and women have authority over the rest of creation, 'dominion' in the authorized version. Does that give us the right to do what we like? Colonize the Moon and subdue it, harness its resources, conquer its harsh environment?

The story tellers of Genesis had no idea, of course, that the Moon was a great world in its own right, a gigantic ball of rock larger than Europe, two thousand miles in diameter, slowly spinning round the Earth. The world for them was a small haven of order in a vast and dark ocean of chaos, protected from the waters above by a roof-like dome, the firmament of heaven. The Sun was a light, beneath the dome of the sky, illuminating their world from within. The Moon was merely a lesser light for the night. They had no way of knowing otherwise.

The biblical creation stories were written, without any *scientific* knowledge, to express the Israelites' revolutionary belief that One God was Creator of Heaven and Earth, the land, the sea and everything in them. In the millennia since then, we have learnt a great deal about the universe, and in particular we have learnt much more about the Moon, what it is in itself. The first telescopes, early in the seventeenth century, revealed great mountain ranges, and enormous craters, bright highlands and grey deserts. Within half a century, the Italian astronomer Riccioli had named the mysterious dark areas 'seas' – *mare* in Latin.

We now know that the so called 'seas' are the scars left on the face of the Moon from the formation of the lunar landscape. Four billion years ago, giant asteroids collided with Earth's satellite, dug holes so deep and released so much energy that thousands of square miles of rugged surface melted into seas of lava, wiping out ancient craters and mountain ranges. These seas of lava soon solidified as the dark patches we have come to identify as the face of the Man in the Moon. (Personally, I always had a problem with this: however much I tried I could not make myself see a face! A man with a gun and a dog – but never a face. That is until I went to Australia. There we see the Moon the other way up. Out in the bush one night, watching an Aboriginal dance troupe perform their story of creation, imitating the emu, the kangaroo, and the crocodile, I looked up and saw, with astonishment, a ghostly face staring down at us!)

The naming of features on the Moon has added its own poetry: The Sea of Tranquillity (where man left his first lunar footprint in 1969), the Ocean of Storms, the Bay of Rainbows, the Sea of Nectar and the Sea of Clouds. Murmured on a windy night when earthly clouds race across the sky, causing the bright Moon to flare and fade, they bring a new depth of beauty to the night.

So, in biblical fashion, we have named the craters, mountain ranges and rocky deserts of the Moon. But should we go further? NASA, of course, was 'over the moon' as it were, at the discovery of water at the lunar poles. With the public showing dwindling interest in space exploration, NASA was in danger of facing major cuts in funding from Congress. A few million tons of water changed all that. A whole new range of opportunities opened up.

The press responded rapidly to the news. Papers were full of artists' impressions of lunar bases: hi-tech igloos sprouting like mushrooms on the floors of craters, astronauts bouncing about in their bulky space suits, large-wheeled mining equipment trundling across the dusty lunar surface extracting water locked as ice in the soil. All this beneath a black star-studded sky, a blazing Sun and Mother Earth, a great blue and white bubble, hanging silently above the horizon. For many readers these scenes are charged with excitement. A new age dawns. Men and women face the challenge of the High Frontier.

The Moon, it is argued, is the gateway to the rest of the solar system, a low gravity staging post for refuelling. Water deposits make it feasible to colonize our satellite, providing much that is needed to sustain life at a lunar base (liquid for drinking and for growing vegetables; a source of oxygen for breathing, and of both oxygen and hydrogen for rocket fuel), without the great expense of having to transport all these things from Earth.

Telescopes built on the far side of the Moon, shielded from Earth, would give an unequalled view of the cosmos, free from the ever increasing light and radio pollution, experienced by earth-bound astronomers. In the interests of science, it is argued, we have a *duty* to colonize the Moon.

And then there are those retired billionaires who would be happy to spend some of their savings on a new unique form of tourism, skiing, perhaps, in low gravity in futuristic playgrounds for the rich.

Whatever it all costs, however, it will undoubtedly cost more than either governments or the public expects. It will take money which might otherwise have been diverted to improving education, solving problems of urban poverty, funding cancer research, or targeted at the periodic famines which cripple whole populations of millions. Those who cry 'Leave the Moon alone' are not only concerned about the pollution of a romantic dream: they question whether we are ready yet to leave Mother Earth, with so many problems still unresolved. Where are our priorities?

Space exploration may be inevitable, rather like the discovery of the New World or the conquest of the Antarctic. But if man sets up colonies at the lunar poles, will we ever again gaze with wonder at the fine crescent of a New Moon in the twilight sky, or marvel at the apparent size of a great orange Harvest Moon rising above the haze of an autumn evening?

Questions to consider

1. How would we argue against the view that we should solve our problems on Earth before spending money on exploring the Moon?

2. Should we leave the Moon alone? If so, then why?

3. The Moon, as our nearest neighbour, may well become the base camp for the conquest of space. What do we think of the belief that mankind has a scientific and moral duty to explore space?

4. How realistic is the argument that the exploration of the solar system, beginning with the Moon, will unite nations in a common task and interest and bring an end to war?

5. Does it spoil the Moon to know that men have already walked and driven on its surface? (Neil Armstrong's footprints still lie in the Sea of Tranquillity.)

15

Rising Mars Creates Sports Champions

Planetary influence at birth discovered

French scientist and statistician Michel Gauquelin discovered, in 1955, an interesting bump in his graph relating planetary positions and the hour of birth of six thousand prominent French citizens. In fact there were two bumps. For years, Gauquelin had pursued the 'grain of truth' that might lurk within the claims of astrology – that the heavens influence our lives. What he found was consistent and surprising. The statistics revealed that if you plot the position of the planet Mars at the moment of birth, of people who, later in life, excel in sport or in military careers, the planet is more likely than not, either to be rising at the time, or else (the second bump) just passing its highest point in the sky. The results were significant in a statistical sense – i.e. not merely a chance fluctuation.

The painstaking research was expanded to include famous citizens of other European countries and then to cover an equivalent list from the USA. The results were always the same. Mars seems to have some hand in the careers of champion sportsmen or exceptional military leaders. The 'Mars effect' disappeared when the birth records of ordinary citizens were used; or when the birth had been 'unnatural', either induced or by caesarean. No satisfactory explanation has been found.

For most of us, astrology means the daily horoscope in the evening paper. 'Virgo: A good week to explore new friendships'; 'Capricorn: beware of getting too involved in money matters until after the weekend'. General support and encouragement to boost the feel-good factor of the readers, with gentle warnings thrown in to keep the balance. Harmless entertainment, not taken too seriously by anyone.

Or is it harmless? Astrology has become big business, and more star forecasts are read daily than ever before in history. Many believe in the influence of the stars passionately, and allow their lives and their public decisions to be moulded by an astrologer's predictions. (Even a President of the USA may be affected: the news that an astrologer regularly advised Nancy Reagan caused much disquiet.) And nowadays every teenage magazine has to have its own 'Your Stars' section.

Astrologers defend their position by claiming to have access to scientific laws, based on millennia of experience; occult laws that govern our day to day lives. They claim to reveal the truth.

Modern scientists, particularly astronomers, tend to take a very different view and reject astrology out of hand, as absurd. There are no known laws of nature that could provide any possible link between what happens in the sky, as the Sun, Moon and planets move through the constellations, and the fluctuations of fortune in our private lives. To believe otherwise is to dabble in superstition, ignorance and irrational rubbish. Just as alchemy died out and was replaced by modern chemistry, so astrology should have given way to the science of astronomy long ago.

Yet, astrology survives and flourishes, despite (or helped by?) the rational opposition of almost every scientist. This fact needs some explanation.

Astrology has a long and venerable history. It began with the Chaldeans about four thousand years ago. It was they who first allocated stars to their constellations and mapped out the signs of the zodiac. It was magi 'from the east' who read the heavens and concluded that a child, worth visiting, had been born in Israel. (There is much speculation about the star of

Bethlehem, but it is doubtful if we shall ever know what it was they saw. One possibility, which makes 'astrological' sense, is that in the year 5 BC, the year Jesus is thought to have been born, Saturn, the planet associated with Israel, moved into Israel's sign, Pisces, and was followed by Jupiter, the planet of royalty. Any astrologer of the day could have concluded that this meant a king would be born in Israel.)

In the Middle Ages, every Christian scholar assumed that events on earth reflect changes in the sky. According to one of the most admired philosophers of the past, Aristotle, everything that happens in the sub-lunary world is caused and governed by the motions of the heavenly bodies. It comes, then, as no surprise to find that the first astronomers in the sixteenth and seventeenth centuries were also astrologers. Kepler, discoverer of the laws of planetary motion (without which we could never have landed on the Moon, or sent space shots to Jupiter and beyond), produced an astrological calendar and towards the end of his days became court astrologer to the Duke of Wallenstein.

Kepler expressed satisfaction when one of his prophecies, of a cold spell, came true. ' In the Alpine farms people die of the cold. It is reliably reported that when they arrive home and blow their noses, the noses fall off . . .' But he also had his doubts. He considered popular astrology to be a dreadful superstition based on faulty foundations, while still clinging to the view that somewhere, beneath the quackery, there was something true. The search for this truth he likened to a hen scratching in an evil-smelling dunghill for a decent grain of corn. 'That the sky does something to man is obvious enough: but what it does specifically remains hidden.'

It was to find this grain of truth that Michel Gauquelin compared thousands of birth dates with character traits and careers, and found the apparent link between the rising of the planet Mars and success in sport. He found other links. Jupiter governs politicians and actors in a similar way, while the rising Moon has an influence on writers, and the planet Saturn has some sort of fairy godmother control over the careers of scientists. In each case the heavenly body is either rising at the time of birth or is culminating – passing its high point in the sky. And as with Mars, the influence is small, appearing as no more than a slight bump in the statistics of prominent and successful people. The rest of us are lost in a fuzz of meaningless data!

It can be interesting to get a group of people to write the four names, Moon, Mars, Jupiter, Saturn in a list and then ask them which heavenly body might have some influence over the four professions, politician, sportsman, writer, and scientist. The majority of people will associate them in the ways discovered in the statistics quoted above, illustrating how deeply the mythology of astrology has seeped into our subconscious, whether or not we happen to believe in it. (Gauquelin pursued his discovery of a link between Jupiter and politicians, whom he considered to be tough-minded, and found that an astonishingly high percentage of Nazi leaders in the Third Reich had been born at the rising or culmination of that major planet.)

Scientists, who rule out astrology as absurd, without giving it any further thought, are stuck for an alternative explanation for Gauquelin's results. Perhaps, it is suggested, some demographic law is at work: though no one, so far, has been able to discover what the law might be. One thing that has surely been ruled out is the gravitational attraction of the heavenly body. Although the Moon might have some significant pull, it has been calculated that the gravitational tug of a fifty kilogram midwife moving round the delivery bed is stronger than anything Mars could exert even at its closest encounters with Earth!

So we are left with some unexplained, though intriguing, statistics concerning one aspect of the lives of a minority of successful people. A very rickety basis for predicting anything useful about the personalities and day-to-day problems of the average magazine reader. And as we all know, statistics can be notoriously misleading even when produced by honest, well-intentioned researchers.

Total non-believers in astrology may take comfort, however, from other results of Gauquelin's research. When he looked for statistical support for a link between personality traits and star signs he found absolutely no correlation at all. A so-called Virgo type may be born in any month of the year and if anything is more likely to born under at least three signs other than Virgo. Statistics give no support for the 'Your Star' section of the evening paper.

Astronomers could have predicted this negative result from their general knowledge of star charts. The signs of the zodiac are man-made and nothing to do with the stars themselves. As the Earth orbits the Sun, the Sun appears to move through the heavens and its yearly track is divided up, for convenience, into twelve sections. The groups of stars in these divisions are the constellations of the Zodiac: Aries, Taurus, Gemini, Cancer, Leo, Virgo, Libra, Scorpio, Sagittarius, Capricorn, Aquarius, Pisces and back to Aries again. The sky was divided up that way, four thousand years ago, by Chaldean astronomers. We have inherited their pattern making and it is the basis for the astrology of star signs. But astronomers in different cultures, such as the Chinese or the Incas, created other patterns from the random scattering of stars (rather as one person might 'see' a ship in the clouds on a summer day, while their friend 'sees' a dragon).

The fact that a thirteenth constellation, Ophiuchus, the Serpent Holder, is wedged between Scorpio and Sagittarius has for some reason always been ignored by astrologers, suggesting that even in their eyes, the 'star signs' are only rather loosely attached to the sky! (This long known fact was 'discovered' by the press in 1997 causing a temporary sensation.)

But there is an even more inconvenient truth than the awkwardness of Ophiuchus, which is also ignored by astrologers. Due to a phenomenon called precession each star sign has slipped backwards into the previous constellation. When

astrology first began, the Sun was 'in' Aries in the spring as it
crossed the equator at the Spring Equinox on its journey up
the sky from winter to summer (in the Northern Hemisphere).
But the Earth's axis does a slow twenty-six thousand-year
wobble which means that the positions of the poles and the
line of the equator, as projected on to the sky, are always on
the move. Two thousand years ago the sign of Aries slid back
into Pisces. It is now on the verge of sliding further into
Aquarius (hence the dawning of the 'Age of Aquarius'). The
sign of Aquarius is in Capricorn, that of Capricorn in Scorpio
and so on.

The star signs drifted, long ago, away from their stellar
moorings and now only relate to the seasons of the year. If
they tell us anything, then it is perhaps that it is the weather
and the day-length, not the stars, which are significant when
we are born. Children born in summer, when they can be put
outside in prams to breath fresh air and experience lots of
light, have a different start in life from children born in winter
who have to be wrapped up against the cold and spend more
time in the dark. A 'Leo' is a summer child, a 'Scorpio' a
winter child and they will develop their particular personalities from those beginnings. But the stars have no more affect
on the lives of these or other babies than they do in causing
'influenza' (once believed to be due to the 'influence' of the
stars); or in sending disasters (the word 'disaster' having
'astrum', the Latin for star, at its root.)

Given that astrology has no basis in science, its continued
popularity says something important and interesting about
people. Those who dismiss it all as total rubbish are likely to
explain its appeal as a sad consequence of the ignorance of
those who are unable to distinguish pseudo-science from true
science. Astrology's claim to be working with a body of law,
built up from millennia of observation and experience, combined with the use of computers in casting horoscopes, makes
it all sound very scientific, it is argued, to those who are
gullible. This sort of dismissal does not go deep enough.

It is very hard being a human being. Sometimes we feel lost. Life can seem empty, hollow, and without purpose. These low points in our days, or years, are not merely unfortunate blips in our personal stories; they are a significant part of the human condition. It is not obvious to us, all the time, what we are about; or even who we are.

Astrology attempts to answer these troubling questions by asserting that there *is* a pattern and order to our lives. It responds to a deep instinctive feeling that each of us has a significant place in the scheme of things. The appeal of astrology is that it seems to tell us a little about who we are, where we come from, and where we are going. It affirms that our lives have meaning. But it does so by treating the stars and planets as divine powers, which they are not, and so may ultimately lead us badly astray.

Questions to consider

1. How would you defend the view that astrology is harmless entertainment? Or is it dangerous?

2. How seriously do people really take their star signs when they check the day's horoscope in their newspaper?

3. Is there any truth in the astrological link between signs of the zodiac and different personalities? Is there, for example, a 'Virgo type'?

4. How would you counsel someone who learned from an astrologer that his horoscope predicted an early death?

5. Is astrology a passing fashion? Will it go the way of alchemy and be seen to be false science – or is it here to stay?

6. What does the persistent interest in astrology tell us about human beings?

16

Angels in Spacesuits

Was God an astronaut?

The skies have been full of unidentified flying objects, UFOs, since the end of the Second World War. In early days they were called flying saucers because of their apparent roundness and the way they seemed to skim across the sky. They were bright, exciting, and inexplicable; and the stories of sightings carried with them the thrill and possibility of visitations by intelligent beings from space. The heavens were suddenly alive with mystery. While organized religion in the West declined, interest in alien spaceships increased. It was as though human beings, deprived of older beliefs in heaven, were turning to the skies for spiritual nourishment, and longing to believe in UFOs. The psychologist C.G. Jung called them 'technological angels'.

One of the marks of a true religion lies in its recognition of the transcendent: it alerts its followers to the reality of things that lie beyond their everyday lives. It suggests that the 'ordinary' is rooted in the 'extraordinary', and that through prayer or meditation one may peer deeper into reality and perceive truths that are missed in the hurly-burly of earning a living, feeding a family or just plain surviving.

It is this sense of the transcendent which separates the great religions (Buddhism, Islam, Christianity and so forth), from non-religious philosophies such as Marxism, Freudianism or Humanism. It is in this longing for the 'Other', whether known as the Kingdom of Heaven, the Divine Presence, Brahman, Nirvana, or the Still Point of the Turning World, that human spirituality finds its goal and fulfilment. Through opening our minds and hearts to the 'Other' we are taken out of ourselves and become centred on the eternal.

The appeal of UFOs to late-twentieth-century people lies in their 'transcendent tug': they are full of other-worldly mystery; they come from the heavens; they suggest a level of intelligence way beyond our own. And if they are of a kindly disposition they may bring salvation from the skies, a latter-day version of the Second Coming, 'The Son of Man coming in the clouds with great power and glory'.

The rational sceptic will dismiss claims that UFOs are alien spacecraft as a naïve case of mistaken identity. They are either natural phenomena (meteors, freak clouds, the planet Venus, ball lightning, electrical discharges, optical illusions), or man-made but unidentified objects (weather balloons, top-secret experimental warplanes, satellites). The UFO enthusiast, however, will reject such a view as 'explaining away' one of the most important and significant discoveries of the twentieth century – that we are being visited by intelligent beings from other worlds; and have been for several millennia. Governments have all the evidence, apparently, but there is a conspiracy of silence.

When I put it to a firm believer in alien visitations that what we were seeing in the current craze for UFO sightings was really (quoting Jung) a modern science-fiction version of mediaeval angels, he shook his head firmly. 'No, no! You've got it the wrong way round! Their *angels* were really *aliens*. They were space travellers, but the only way people could understand them in the past was to speak of them as angels.'

'So the archangel Gabriel and all the other angels in the nativity stories of Matthew and Luke were really astronauts from another planet?' I queried cautiously.

'Oh yes!' he nodded with absolute certainty.

The theory that God himself was an astronaut is already thirty years old. Erich von Daniken wrote his best seller *Chariots of the Gods?* in 1968, giving a new spin to the whole of religious history. The legendary giants who mated with the daughters of men in Genesis were Martians, their gigantic size attributed to the planet's weak gravity. The angels who spoke with Abraham and called down fire on Sodom and Gomorra were aliens; the catastrophe that burnt up the immoral cities a nuclear explosion. The prophet Elijah, taken up into the sky in a fiery chariot, became one of the first cases of the abduction of a human being in a spacecraft. And most intricate of all was the spaceship described by Ezekiel in his vision of God recorded in the first chapter of his book.

The prophet Ezekiel was with the dispirited exiles in Babylon after the destruction of the Temple in Jerusalem by Nebuchadnezzar, in the sixth century BC. It seemed at the time that their national and religious life was over. They were dead as a people. But Ezekiel had an encouraging and challenging vision. God arrived in their midst in a blaze of light and a roar of thunder. He came from the north (the way the exiles had been dragged by their captors) on a giant four-wheeled chariot, each wheel in the control of a strange mythical four-faced beast. The description of this marvellous vehicle reads very like that of one of the great festival juggernauts used by the Babylonians to tow their gods, Bel and Nebo, around the town. There was one major difference: the wooden Babylonian gods needed oxen to get them moving; the God of the Hebrews carried the whole of history on his back and moved however he willed. The refugees, grieving by the waters of Babylon, must have been glad to learn from Ezekiel, through his symbolic vision, that despite the disastrous events, their God had not abandoned them.

Von Daniken interpreted the passage differently. He read it as an accurate eyewitness account of the landing of a space-ship, supporting his theory that God was an astronaut. Piloting this remarkable craft was one whose form had the 'appearance of a human being': not surprisingly, since he also believed that Genesis tells us that the 'Elohim' made humans in their own image in the first place. Aliens have not only visited us – they also created us.

Von Daniken found more evidence for his beliefs in other ancient cultures. It was space travellers who left the mysterious markings on the dry deserts of Peru; it was an astronaut in launch position, not a god, whose picture was carved on a temple of the Mayas in Central America; it was alien engineers who taught the Egyptians how to build pyramids. Any unsolved archaeological problem becomes grist for the mill, evidence of extra-terrestrial intelligence. *Chariots of the Gods?* caught the mood of the times and became a best seller.

A common theme unites many of the modern UFO cults: the space visitors come with a warning and a message of salvation at a time of great ecological crisis. The human race is in danger of ruining the planet, through the misuse of resources or the deployment of nuclear weapons. Now is the time that we desperately need help. Ruth Norman, known as Queen Uriel to the flying saucer group Unarius, proclaimed, before she died at the great age of ninety-three, that a spacefleet of starships of the Space Brothers will land on 'Home Globe' Earth in the year 2001. They will bring education and super science to guide blundering humans, and will transform the world through advanced technology. Uriel herself (Queen of the Archangels) claimed that in a past life she was the daughter of Pharaoh who found Moses in the bull rushes; and in another incarnation she was Mary Magdelene. She would regularly lead her followers in 'regression sessions' to help them remember the days when they were all together living on Atlantis; and before that when they shared great times on a distant planet in the constellation of Orion.

The Aetherius Society based in London has a slightly different brief. Once more humans are in great need of help, but this time the focus is on evil forces lurking in the galaxy. Jesus is alive and well and living on the planet Venus; King Arthur is on Saturn. Aetherius, a sort of cosmic Archangel, supported by the crew of a six-kilometre long spaceship docked in orbit around Mars, keeps an eye on our part of the solar system. Initial contact with these beings was made by

George King, who heard a voice speaking to him in Maida Vale telling him that he was to be the mouthpiece of an inter-planetary parliament. Followers are encouraged to take part in the cosmic war between good and evil by joining together in prayer sessions known as 'Spiritual Pushes'. In this way the Earth was saved, for example in 1956, from a terrible invasion of intelligent fish people from the far side of the galaxy.

The fastest growing area of interest in 'technological angels' is probably in the realm of UFO abductions. Abductees claim to have been whisked away by aliens, from their cars when driving on their own late at night, or from their beds. The experiences are compelling but dream-like, sometimes for-gotten and only discovered under hypnosis. (Some would say that this is a predominantly hypnotist-driven phenome-non.) The aliens are often described as having high foreheads, large unblinking eyes and shining clothes; they examine their captives intimately, probing and prodding and showing par-ticular interest in the sex of the abductee. The victims return with a message for the world; that we must be kinder to one another, or that the nations should stop warring if we are to avoid an apocalyptic catastrophe. They frequently speak of the experience in religious terms.

One survey makes the incredible claim (surely exagge-rated?) that 3.7 million Americans have been abducted by aliens!

There is a great similarity between the stories of abductees who have been in contact with aliens and the accounts given by nineteenth-century spiritualist mediums. The mediums used trance to make contact with the spirits of the dead or superior beings: Red Indian chiefs or Masters of the Great White Brotherhood who had messages of guidance for the world. The introduction of UFOs and aliens adds a sort of hi-tech, Star Trek, element to the scenario – with a touch of Star Wars. It all seems, to the outsider, to be a world of make-believe.

The growth of new religious movements based on stories of

alien visitations coincides with the scientific search for extra-terrestrial life and may even be masking a very significant scientific debate. Writers have often speculated imaginatively about the possibility of life on other worlds. Now, for the first time in history, we are in a good position to make some realistic discoveries. The list of stars detected, by astronomers, to have planets orbiting them, is increasing in length; and only the local population has been examined. There may be nothing unique about Earth. Organic compounds, the chemical bases of life, turn up throughout the universe. It begins to look as though chemistry has its own self-organizing properties and that life will be found to have blossomed elsewhere. The search for extra-terrestrial intelligence, SETI, has become an established programme amongst radio astronomers, both professional and amateur.

It is of course true that *homo sapiens* may be the first intelligent radio-broadcasting species in the universe. The universe has a progressive evolving history, beginning with the Big Bang. For life to evolve, carbon and other higher elements had to be created by nuclear fusion in the first generation of massive stars. Only then could organic compounds come together and biological evolution begin. Some worlds will be ahead of others and *someone* has to be the first to begin to think scientifically. It may be us, and we shall listen in vain to the skies. It could take thousands or millions of years for life elsewhere to catch up.

On the contrary, however, we may be the late developers and very soon the phone will ring and we shall be caught wondering whether to answer it or not.

Questions to consider

1. Christian theology sees Jesus Christ as the unique incarnation of the Word of God on Earth. If we discover that the human race is not the only manifestation of intelligence in the universe, that there are other civilizations on other worlds, will the Christian tradition be able to accommodate the view that there have been other divine incarnations in this and other galaxies? Or will a unique gospel radiate out from Earth and *only* Earth?

2. What harm is there in believing that we are being watched over by a superior intelligent race from some other world? If we conclude that all stories of alien visitations or abductions are purely imagination should we make every effort to stop other people believing in them?

3. What is so compelling about the possibility that we might be raised to a higher level of consciousness through encounters with extra-terrestrial intelligence or through evolution? Are we lacking something as human beings?

4. Why do so many people *want* to believe that UFOs are the vehicles of alien astronauts? And how much truth is there in the suggestion that, deep down, we are scared of finding that we are all alone in a vast and impersonal universe?

17

Final Episode

It is remarkable how often groups of people get caught up in the belief that the world is about to come to an end: not only the lonely cartoon figure with a sandwich board, shouting 'The End is Nigh!' Whole sects and cults get carried away by a sense of impending doom. It is almost as though they wanted it all to end or, at least, felt some deep-seated need for it to end. They have always been wrong.

In a very limited personal sense their fears may, of course, have been well founded. Members of The Branch Dravidian cult (an extremist offshoot of the Seventh Day Adventists) were led by David Koresh to believe, in 1994, that the final battle with evil was about to be fought, as history came to a close. Almost all of them were burnt to death when a badly-handled siege by the FBI went wrong.

In 1997 Marshall Applewhite, with thirty-eight of his followers, committed suicide, in California, to join the UFO they believed to be shadowing the comet Hale-Bopp as it swung through the solar system. Applewhite had convinced his devotees that the world was a garden for growing souls, whose destiny was to rise to a level above the human. Anyone who did not make this leap to the next level would be 'spaded under'. Their tragic self-propelled exit was accelerated by his warnings that it was the last chance to evacuate planet Earth.

Applewhite and Koresh probably believed what they taught. Other cult leaders clearly do not. They are in the busi-ness for gain: false prophets in an obvious sense. The follow-

ing headline appeared in *The Independent* newspaper in
November 1992:

DOOMSDAY PREACHER JAILED

Seoul (Reuter) – A 'Doomsday' preacher was jailed for two
years for defrauding his followers after persuading them the
world would start coming to an end last October. Although
Lee Jang-rim, 46, had apologized, he should be punished
for the harm he caused his followers, Judge Soh Sang-kyu
said.

Many of Lee's followers quit their jobs, sold their homes,
gave their assets to his church and left their families in the
belief they would be lifted to Heaven before pestilence
swept the Earth.

Millennium fever will no doubt generate more doomsday
preachers as we reach the year 2000. Something in the human
make-up seems to respond to rumours of doom at critical
moments of history (as though it is safest to imagine the
worst): rumours that appeal to uneasy feelings of paranoia
and of guilt, both of these demons lurking in the human
psyche; devils waiting to pounce and ensnare the unwary. The
unscrupulous will use them to manipulate followers and control their allegiance. But some cult leaders will be convinced of
the truth of their message that the end of the world is at hand
– slaves, perhaps, to their own troubled psyches. Outsiders
will label them fanatics.

And yet, all these rumours of doom have a respectable
history. Many are rooted in the biblical notion that one day
justice will be seen to be done, that God will finally show his
hand and not allow great evils to go unpunished. The End of
the World and Judgment Day are bedded deep in the Jewish,
Christian and Muslim traditions. The prophet Joel wrote in
powerful poetry of the Day of the Lord:

The Sun will be turned into darkness,
   and the Moon into blood,
before the Day comes,
   that great and terrible Day (Joel 3.4).

The New Testament picks up the theme and ends with
the chilling drama of the Great Day of God's retribution,
described in colourful and nightmarish detail in the Book of
Revelation. The Four Horseman of the Apocalypse appear,
riding their white, red, black and pale horses, bringing death
and destruction; bowls of God's anger are emptied over the
Earth by angels; the grapes of God's wrath are trampled; the
final battle at Armageddon is announced; and a star called
Wormwood falls to Earth, poisoning a third of the seas. (A
disturbing detail for many Russian Christians in 1986 because
Wormwood in Russian is Chernobyl. Lakes and streams as far
away as Lapland were polluted with radiation, when the
nuclear reactor exploded. It was particularly worrying for
those who looked for signs, when the disaster was soon
followed by eclipses of the Sun and of the Moon.)

Interestingly, Jesus warned against any over hasty guess-
work as to when the world would end. Although he uses the
traditional poetry of the prophets to discuss it (sun darkened,
stars falling from the sky), he himself does not know when it
will happen; only the Father knows (Mark 13). This clear
statement has not stopped the speculation or the attempts to
find a secret code or to read between the lines of scripture. If
the quotations in Mark 13 are accurate, then, Jesus gave the
distinct impression that a lot of history would have to happen
before the end came; wars and rumours of wars, earthquakes
and famines – and that just the beginning of the process. The
other important passage, in which Jesus uses the current
mythology of an impending Judgment Day, is in the radical
parable of the separation of the sheep from the goats
(Matthew 25). The astonishment that runs through the
scenario is with the criteria by which people enter, or fail to

enter, the Kingdom of Heaven. These criteria have exclusively to do with whether or not compassion has been shown to another person in need (feeding the hungry, visiting the sick and imprisoned . . .) with no reference to the observance of religious rules or rituals. It must have come as a shock to many religious people.

The Qur'an continues the tradition of using vivid imagery to describe the end of the world. Running through the Surahs is the continual reminder, 'Remember the days of Noah!' God destroyed the world once with a great flood. What God has done before he can do again. Judgment Day waits just around the corner.

When the sun ceases to shine; when the stars fall down and the mountains are blown away; when camels big with young are left untended and the wild beasts are brought together; when the seas are set alight and men's souls are reunited; when the infant girl, buried alive, is asked for what crime she was thus slain; when the records of men's deeds are laid open and the heaven is stripped bare; when Hell burns fiercely and Paradise is brought near: then each soul shall know what it has done (Surah: The Cessation).

Other cultures, quite separately and uninfluenced by these Western traditions, expressed similar fears and also fantasized about a dramatic end to history. In Norse mythology, a monstrous wolf swallows the sun, plunging the land into a terrible winter, as a prelude to the culmination of the world story: a final battle between the gods and the giants at Ragnarok. The whole world is set ablaze as the ground shakes and crumbles, and stars fall from the sky like weary swallows tumbling into the sea. Even the gods are killed. Wagner revisited this myth in his opera *Götterdämmerung*, 'The Twilight of the Gods'.

Other doom-laden scenarios were woven by a totally different culture on the opposite side of the Atlantic. The

Aztecs believed that the world had already ended several times before, with disastrous floods or locked in the grip of ice and freezing fog. The next catastrophe, they calculated with great precision, will strike on the 23 December 2012, when the world will end in fire.

Fire, ice age, deluge, earthquake, darkness, falling stars. It is not hard to detect, in all these myths, primitive (and realistic) fears of unpredictable natural catastrophes. Even in the twentieth century, with all our scientific knowledge of the way the world works, we have not been able to prevent millions dying from earthquake, volcano, flood, storm or tempest. (Fortunately, no one in recorded history has yet been killed by a falling 'star', though the dinosaurs were wiped out by one.) It is not surprising that the human psyche has, lurking within it, feelings of dread that something awful is about to happen.

Inevitably the entertainment industry has cashed in on these fears, turning terror into fun. Tabloids regularly trawl through the writings of the sixteenth-century astrologer Nostradamus to see if he has hidden some message of doom in his strange verses. So, 23 March 1986 was supposed, on the bases of Quatrain 5 in Century 2, to be the date of the beginning of the third, and final, World War. The day came and went as usual, as days do. And the interpretation of the verse which describes a man arriving in a fish, carrying messages of war – the planets Mercury (messages) and Mars (war) moving into the constellation Pisces (fish), which happened in March that year – went with all other astrological predictions into the rubbish bin.

Film producers, too, cannot resist the temptation to titillate our fears. Using brilliant state-of-the-art computer graphics they make willing voyeurs of us all, as giant meteorites exterminate millions, or volcanoes erupt in Los Angeles. And there are moves afoot, it is rumoured, to turn Megiddo in Israel, traditional site of Armageddon – the final battle between the forces of good and evil – into a theme park.

Feelings of dread that something awful is about to happen

have become more precise with the development of science. We have a growing body of knowledge about ice ages and the way they may be triggered. We watch space and map the trajectories of asteroids the size of mountains that fly perilously close to planet Earth (in the near future we will develop the technology to protect ourselves from such unwanted visitors). We monitor earthquakes and volcanoes and issue timely warnings. But we begin to suspect that when it comes to it, it might be we, the human race, who will be the cause of the final episode of world history.

The population explosion combined with global warming, due to our polluting of the atmosphere, could lead to a catastrophe of unimaginable proportions. We could turn the world into an uninhabitable desert. Or a disease, like AIDS, might spread beyond our control, and the world population crash like a community of rabbits succumbing to myxomatosis. But the scenario that periodically troubles us most is the threat of biological, chemical or nuclear war.

There is enough madness in those who live for power politics, in journalists who whip up nationalist feelings, in the deranged hearts of (too many) dictators, and in the blind greed of the armaments industry, to make any rational person nervous when contemplating the proliferation of nuclear weapons. It is no wonder we are haunted by the shadow of the mushroom cloud.

But then none of these threats would bring an *end* to the world: even global nuclear war. Probably, some people would survive, plunged back into a new Stone Age, and civilization would have to start all over again. Supposing it were worse, and the nuclear winter, predicted to follow an all-out nuclear exchange, were to wipe out mankind, what then? Life would survive. It would be, it has been suggested, a world of weeds, rats and cockroaches. A similar thing happened once before. When the dinosaurs died out sixty-five million years ago, the land was dominated for millions of years by ferns; and amongst the ferns were small rat-sized furry mammals from which evolution generated all the mammal species we see today, including ourselves. A set-back indeed. But not the end of the world, if by world we mean the planet. Life has a way of finding its way around the most massive of challenges.

Is it only fear and insecurity that makes us fantasize about impending disaster? There is something surprisingly un-Christian about it (some scenes in the Book of Revelation not withstanding). In the early church, the small communities of St Paul's time, there was a tremendous sense that all was going to be well. 'In my estimation,' wrote Paul (Rom. 8), 'all that we suffer in the present time is nothing in comparison with the glory which is destined to be disclosed to us, for the whole creation is waiting with eagerness for the children of God to be revealed.' Christ would return at the Parousia, Heaven would come down to Earth (Rev. 21), and the world would enjoy a glorious transformation.

We don't seem to hear much from those who proclaim the end of the world about the possibility of a glorious transformation. Is it not reasonable for Christians to believe that, in time, all things will work out well? Not might but *will*.

Our world, planet Earth, has a long way to go before approaching its end. It seems a pity to want to wrap up history with a last episode as though it was a soap opera. Modern cosmology tells us with confidence that the Sun will continue to burn steadily as a yellow dwarf star for at least as long as it has been shining so far. Short of the planet being knocked out of its orbit by a wandering rogue planet, ejected from some other solar system, or by a dead red dwarf star careering through our corner of space (both incredibly unlikely events), there is nothing to suppose that the planet will not survive along with the Sun. It then has five billion years of spinning to look forward to!

The end, when it does come, will be dramatic. The Sun will burn up all its inner reserves of hydrogen and then undergo a transformation. It will cool slightly and become a red giant star. Expanding, its surface will rise like a great tide, until the flame fields of the photosphere come lapping at the shores of Earth. Our Earth and Moon, spiralling into the fiery depths, will turn into incandescent gas and evaporate. And the Sun will reclaim that to which it gave light and life in the first place.

In five billion years.

Time to make plans.

Time for a glorious transformation.

Questions to consider

1. Is it hard to believe that all will be well, and that the world will enjoy a glorious transformation?

2. What are the chances that mankind will be around in five billion years?

3. How is it that people are so easily persuaded to believe that the end of the world is about to come?

4. When scripture refers to the Day of the Lord, were the writers thinking in terms of a literal historical date; or were they thinking in metaphors?

18

Universe Doomed

Catastrophic end to comos predicted

The fate of the universe is much discussed by astronomers. Some predict, with confidence, that one day, in the distant future, long after the incineration of planet Earth and the death of the Sun, the universe itself will face a final conflagration: a disaster far more dramatic than anything imagined by Norse story tellers when they conjured up the twilight of the gods at Ragnarok.

Galaxies will be torn apart, stars and planets shredded. The cosmos will collapse, roaring backwards into the mother of black holes as the force of gravity, its domain running the length and breadth of the universe, drags everything together again. In a blast of X-rays the glowing remains of cosmic history will rapidly shrink and finally vanish as the dying universe swallows itself, including space and time, leaving nothing.

It is the Big Crunch. It dominates the end of time as the Big Bang does the beginning: an unnerving scenario. All of history, all hopes of human progress, all of culture and civilization, doomed to a final and total extinction.

But don't hang around waiting. We are contemplating the remote horizons of a far off era, eighty thousand million years, at the very least, in the future.

So why get excited?

Part of the answer is that an entirely different fate may await the universe. At the turn of the century, astronomers were totally convinced that the universe would die far more slowly than in the dramatic scenario of the Big Crunch. They imagined that the cosmos would quietly peter out, like the faltering light of a puckering candle flame. Over time, the stars, including the sun, would burn up all their stored energy, slowly dwindle and die. The cosmos would fade away through a long lingering twilight, getting colder and colder until the last lights went out. They called it the Heat Death. Arctic nights in the depths of Ice Ages could only whisper with frozen breath of the terrible darkness to come: the universe immobilized, locked for ever in the eternal grip of a terminal deep freeze.

It all depends on how much matter there is in, and between, the galaxies. And on the old adage 'What goes up, must come down.'

It has become an accepted fact that the universe is expanding. Whichever way astronomers look, as they peer with their telescopes into deep space, they find that distant galaxies are flying away from us at speeds which are difficult to comprehend. The light from these galaxies is shifted to the red end of the spectrum (the 'Red Shift') and gives an accurate measure of the rate of recession. The further away, the faster they fly.

Traced backwards through time, it appears that the whole universe emerged some fifteen thousand million years ago from a primal explosion, the Big Bang. The key question is, how much material did the Big Bang fling out in the expanding universe? The answer is critical. All matter has a gravitational attraction to all other matter: every atom, slice of cheese cake, planet and sun is gently and unremittingly pulling on everything else. If there is enough of the stuff spread out through the cosmos, then it will slowly drag the expansion of the universe to a halt, after which everything will begin to fall together again. What goes up must come down. From then on it is downhill all the way to the Big Crunch.

But there may not be enough material in the universe to set us on the downward path towards the Big Crunch. In fact if we add up the masses of all the visible stars in all the observed galaxies, add to it all possible planetary systems, and then add to that the unimaginable quadrillions of tons of dust and gas that make up the clouds within and between the galaxies, we can, even then, only scrape together 10% of what is needed to halt the expansion of the universe. With nothing to stop the expansion, the universe will continue to fly apart, burning up its energy, galaxies waving goodbye to each other as they grow old, fade and drift off into eternal night.

So, forget the Big Crunch? Well, no! Something is going on that astronomers do not entirely understand. There seems to be more material about in the cosmos than we can see. As swarms of stars, the galaxies, slowly spin through space, they behave as though they are much more massive than they appear to be. Imagine if two dancers were to twirl around a dance floor each holding fast to the other to prevent the partner from flying off into the watching crowd. Now imagine that one partner is invisible. It would be obvious to an observer that the visible dancer had a dancing partner even though that partner was not visible. In a similar way, galaxies would fly apart if they contained no more mass than has so far been observed. But they do not fly apart, and there lies the mystery.

It has been called the Missing Mass. Science journals are continually addressing the matter. What is it, if we cannot see it? And even more important – how much of the stuff is there? Is there enough to halt the expansion of the universe and so save us from the long lingering death of an eternal Ice Age?

Many suspects have been named as the invisible partners who dance with the visible galaxies as they twirl their slow pavanes through distant space. Black holes (massive collapsed stars no longer directly visible to telescopes); brown dwarfs (small faint stars outnumbering the regular stars by ten to one); swarms of planet-sized objects (a billion billion Jupiters); clouds of icebergs (the stuff of comets) circling in the outer suburbs of the galaxies; or most exotic, the suggestion that the universe bathes in a cosmic ocean of a form of matter produced in the Big Bang, but so far unknown to science (called WIMPS – weakly interacting massive particles). There seems no end to the imaginative possibilities!

The strangest thing is, it begins to look as though the universe is rather finely balanced: it may turn out to be poised neatly between eternal expansion or eventual collapse. Poised as it were to go either way. Why this should be, no one has satisfactorily explained. (Suppose you, the reader, were a distant descendent of the human race, living at the time when the expansion of the universe had slowed down to almost nothing. And just suppose you had the power to influence which way things worked out. How would you vote – for the Big Crunch or for the Long Dying Twilight?)

The fate of the universe: death or death. Should we bury our heads in the present moment and ignore these long-term predictions, pretend they will never happen? Does the death of the universe, one way or the other, undermine our attempts to make sense of our lives, make everything a waste of time? If in the end it all comes to nothing, why bother?

Questions to consider

1. Is the death of the universe any different, ultimately, from the death of a single person? If so, then in what way?

2. What feelings does contemplation of the death of the universe evoke?

3. Where does heaven fit into this imagined scheme of things?

4. Has God failed if the universe finally collapses in the Big Crunch, or freezes in a Long Dying Twilight? How are his plans or purposes in creation fulfilled if it all ends in death?

19

It's a Mystery

The assumption that science dispels mystery is one of the most stubborn prejudices of the twentieth century. The prejudice runs something like this. Human beings have lived their lives for the most of history, until very recently, wearing a cloak of ignorance. Long ago they were scared of thunder and lightning, thinking that angry gods hid within the clouds; they imagined that another god carried the Sun in a chariot across the sky from dawn to dusk. They believed that illness was caused by evil spirits and that madness and epilepsy were devil possession. They conjured up angels to push the planets around the ecliptic, thinking that without these angelic forces the planets would drift to a halt. They invented a mysterious invisible substance to permeate the universe called the ether, to account for the fact that light waves travel from Sun to Earth through empty space. Whenever our ancestors encountered a mystery, something they could not understand, they invented a god or an angel or a devil or a mysterious substance to explain the phenomenon. Their beliefs were based on ignorance.

Then science comes along and, like the Sun dispersing fog at daybreak, dispels the mysteries with clear scientific explanations. The gods vanish, the angels fly away and the ether turns out to be nothing – an unnecessary hypothesis. Very soon there will be no mysteries left. Science will shine its torch into all the dark corners of ignorance, and on all the mysteries of the universe, and reveal a down-to-earth explanation for everything.

Riding on the back of this prejudice, that science dispels mystery, is a second false assumption: that people only believe in God when they are short of a better explanation for some phenomenon (how the universe emerged from nothing; how the spark of life appeared in a realm of dead chemistry; how the sophisticated design of the human eye came about). Belief in God is the result of ignorance. With no mysteries and everything explained there is no more need for God. Or so the argument runs.

This rather dispiriting prejudice fails to distinguish between two orders of mystery. There are those mysteries which are simply unsolved problems, riddles, conundrums; mysteries which are amenable to solution. The flash and the rumble of thunder no longer mystify us for we know that they are caused by electricity in energetic and highly-charged clouds. Scientific method has indeed resolved many such mysteries and will continue to do so.

But then there is a higher order of mystery which is not dispelled by explanation; a level of mystery which arises from knowledge rather than from ignorance. Richard Feynmann, one of the great physicists of the century, summed it up with the words 'when the phenomenon has been explained the mystery does not go away'. He was speaking of the strange world of quantum mechanics and the bizarre discovery that fundamental particles, the bits that make up atoms, can be described either as waves or as particles. Both descriptions are true even though to normal understanding they appear contradictory. Reality, it seems, is not only mysterious, it is more mysterious than we can imagine.

Knowledge, far from dispelling mystery, can awaken in us a sense of wonder and awe. Science may actually lead us to a religious view of the universe. 'Scientific research,' wrote the French philosopher and mystic Simone Weil, 'is simply a form of religious contemplation.' Many practising scientists and science writers, today, are finding this to be the case; their belief in God arises not from ignorance but from their understanding of the way things are, their discovery of the laws and the mathematics that govern nature. Even when explained, it remains a deeply mysterious universe.

It is true that one of the many reasons given for believing in God has been the inability to explain some aspect of creation. It was never a particularly good reason because it depended on ignorance. The most enduring example, perhaps, has been the difficulty in accounting for the origins of life. Without God's interference, it is argued, the universe would have remained a dismal world of dead chemistry; but God breathed life into it, as he breathed life into Adam in the Garden of Eden, creating a living man out of the dead dust of the Earth. If science finds an explanation for this mystery, then, it is assumed, there is no role left for God.

Once again there is a confusion about the sort of mystery that can be resolved with an explanation and the deeper sense of mystery which remains, even enhanced, when an explanation is given.

Charles Darwin, for lack of experimental evidence, speculated that life first appeared, bacteria-like, in some warm pond and evolved from there into all the rich diversity we see around us. Since then, attempts have been made in the laboratory to recreate the conditions on the early Earth to find out how living processes might have got started. A gaseous mixture of methane and ammonia, with water vapour and hydrogen energized with an electric current to simulate a lightning flash in the atmosphere of the newly formed Earth, and bombarded with ultra-violet light, produces an interesting cocktail of chemistry. The 'fall-out' from this experiment includes amino-acids that are the building bricks of proteins and thus the precursors of life. Slowly a scientific explanation for the origins of life begins to emerge: an explanation that does not smuggle God into the lab to breathe life into the test tube.

More recent work has explored the possibility that the first complex chemistry on the long path to life began in hairline fissures deep in the Earth's crust, drawing energy from sub-terranean heat. Many microbes and even larger organisms have been discovered thriving in conditions which, until recently, would have been thought to be totally hostile to life. Bacteria have been found in rocks more than a kilometre down beneath the surface; alien ecosystems flourish in deep sea trenches, under enormous pressure, far beyond the pene-tration of sunlight, where the water is heated by volcanic vents to over 120° centigrade. We who live at the surface may be the adapted descendants of remote ancestors who came up from a geological hell!

Warm ponds or hell? The answer, it seems, is even stranger.

Current work being done at NASA's Ames Research Centre in California suggests a more ancient and extraordinary origin for life long before there were any little warm ponds on our planet; even predating the birth of the Sun and solar system. Life it seems could have begun in the freezing depths of space where the temperature is below minus 260° centigrade.

Vast clouds of dust and gas, so tenuous that they are equivalent to a vacuum in the laboratory, swirl between the stars. They are a mixture of water, methane, ammonia and carbon monoxide (gases built from the simplest elements in the periodic table, hydrogen, oxygen, nitrogen and carbon). There are traces, too, of other more complex molecules and a fine sprinkling of dust particles. The dust particles are wafted up like soot from the scorching turbulent surfaces of stars; some made of carbon, some of them silicates, some even microscopic diamonds.

The NASA Ames team focussed on the silicates. Simula-tions of the near vacuum of an interstellar dust cloud, 10° above absolute zero, generated some interesting data. The gases began to freeze on the surfaces of the dust grains, like the steam from cooking condensing on a cold window. But grains in space are exposed to ultraviolet light from stars, and when these conditions were reproduced in the laboratory it was found that the gases, frozen in thin layers to the dust grains, underwent a chemical transformation resulting in a profusion of complex organic compounds. Researchers even discovered that curious cell-like structures had been produced, essential in the further evolution of life.

This early chemistry of life, beginning in the dark and frozen reaches of empty space, would not survive long in that harsh environment, were it not protected. Ultraviolet radiation would continually undo what it had accidentally put together. Some of the dust grains, however, would be swept up by comets or asteroids and become buried in dust and ice. Millions of years later, as these comets disintegrated in their orbit round the Sun, their organic chemical cargo would rain down upon the Earth and find a welcome home in its warm ponds and by its volcanic vents.

Our remote ancestors came from space: such a scenario seems increasingly likely. And if it is true, then the whole universe is teeming with the chemical precursors of life, and organic molecules are raining down on to the surfaces of quadrillions of planets throughout the cosmos.

A further refinement to our own story brings in the planet Mars. Four billion years ago, soon after the formation of the solar system, conditions on Mars may have been much more hospitable to life than they were on the early Earth. The beginnings of evolution may have begun there in days when the planet had a protective atmosphere, plenty of water, and was warmer than it is today. Asteroids colliding with Mars, as they did frequently in its early history, will have blasted chunks of rock into space, some of which falling in towards the Sun will have collided with Earth, carrying with them microbes from their home planet. (Several meteorites examined in laboratories seem to have had a Martian origin.) As conditions became more hospitable on Earth, some of these microbes will have survived, thrived, bred and evolved. If this is so, then we are all Martians!

Whatever the scientific explanation for the emergence of

life from dead chemistry, it is a great and remarkable wonder. Mystery is here to stay.

Questions to consider

1. The bread and wine used in the Christian eucharist have sometimes been referred to as the 'mysteries'. Does this have any light to throw on the way we use the term when speaking about the workings of nature?

2. Science and technology are turning the world into one great television audience. What effect is this having upon the way we view mystery?

3. Have you ever felt disappointed when a mystery has been explained? Do scientific explanations spoil the way we feel about the world we live in?

4. Has a scientific explanation ever increased your sense that this is a mysterious universe? What was the subject and how would you describe the mystery to someone else?

20

The Silence of God

The way to be

How are we to speak of God in the twenty-first century, now we have discovered that we are products of an evolving world, in which humans are one small branch of the rich fauna of nature? Meister Eckhart, Dominican mystic of the fourteenth century, said that there is nothing in the world that resembles God so much as silence.

Any attempt to speak of God in an age of science is fraught with difficulties, particularly in view of Eckhart's insight. Much of the discussion becomes a wild and rather hopeless waving of cartoon images to the accompaniment of disclaimers. 'I don't believe in God as an Old Man in the Sky!' (Who does?) Or, 'I can't believe in the jealous God of the Old Testament: he gets mad – and he gets even.'

Descriptions of God in the early parts of the Bible have always posed a problem for Christians. There is charm in the human image of the 'Lord God walking in the garden in the cool of the day'; no charm at all in the ethnic cleansing of Jericho, when the town is put 'under the ban' at God's command, its inhabitants, men women and children, are all slaughtered (except for the family of the prostitute Rahab). There is a touching gentleness about that God-given law in the Torah, which says that if you see your enemy's donkey stumble under its load you are to go to his assistance; but there is a lurking horror in the command that should your son not obey you, you are to take him to the gate of the town, denounce him, and stone him to death.

Yet it is remarkable that despite the public face of the angry lawgiver (created, no doubt, by the religious spin-doctors of the day), the real nature of God remains hidden. The second commandment forbade any carved images: all idols are man-made and God is not like anything in heaven or earth. It even became part of Hebrew tradition not to speak the sacred name.

When the Israelites began to grasp the implications of their belief in one God, they became, perhaps understandably, afraid. The Lord God was no local deity controlled by a priesthood; he had created everything, sparrows, people and mountains; he manipulated the rulers of the earth like chess pieces, moved whole nations, controlled the seas and commanded storms. A tradition developed that no one could see the Lord God in his true form and survive. Confronted by the Almighty, a frail human being would crumble into dust, disintegrate like a moth before a bonfire.

The Israelites, consequently, put some distance between themselves and God; the naked reality of his presence and power was too much to bear. Angels came to their assistance. Many of the biblical characters (Abraham, Jacob, Moses, or the parents of Samson, for example) are said to have spoken with God, but they survived the encounter. In the stories of these meetings God always hides behind a vision, a scaled-down manifestation – an angel. Read, for example, the story of Abraham at the Oak of Mamre, where God promises that Sarah will give birth. The writer alternates between three young men, who represent Yahweh, and Yahweh himself. Or, in the story of Hagar running away from Sarah, when she is directed by God to return home, the angel hovers there like a stage devise, an attempt to portray the impossible.

All our talk of God is an attempt to portray the impossible in language, our minds leaping from cartoon image to cartoon image. Perhaps in the twentieth century, now that our knowledge of the world and its workings is so much more sophisticated than it was in biblical times, we should accept the guidance of Eckhart and recognize God in silence, knowing that he is not like anything else, a mystery hidden by a fog of words.

And yet words are the tools we have for formulating thought. We inherit these pieces of mental furniture from society, along with the rest of culture, and have to make do as best we can. The word 'God' might be compared to a large Victorian sideboard handed down to us from our forebears. Some people love it, polishing it daily; others hate it and want it out of the house; many ignore it, using its surface as a dumping ground for correspondence, dirty clothes and newspapers. Either way, we are stuck with it. Is this word 'God' simply a creation of the mind, a product of human culture, as many atheists argue? Perhaps it just tells us something about human aspirations, giving a sort of focus or goal to the spiritual side of our lives, in a fragile and basically meaningless universe. Or is it a symbol that points beyond itself to a reality that we may encounter, but not imagine?

The fact that we cannot imagine God and always find our words inadequate need not suggest, as the atheist would have it, that there is nothing to describe. Science speaks of many real things in the universe, which are virtually impossible to imagine: that time had a beginning with the Big Bang, making nonsense of questions about what was there before; that the whole of interstellar space emerged from a singularity the size of a pea; that the universe is of limited size but has no boundaries; that the inner world of the atom is so empty that the world's largest building could sit on the head of a pin if all the fundamental particles making up its atoms were forced together. And how do we cope with black holes, for the existence of which there is now an overwhelming amount of evidence? When massive stars reach the end of their lives they collapse under the crushing power of their own gravity, until they disappear from view because even light cannot escape them. We all know what it is like trying to squash too many clothes into a suitcase: but if all the material that makes up planet Earth were crushed into a black hole it would occupy a volume the size of a child's marble, two centimetres in diameter. Such incredible conditions and forces must challenge the powers of imagination of any mind, however brilliant.

Our modern brains were evolved tens of thousands of years ago to cope with survival on the savannahs of East Africa. We have now developed our scientific knowledge far beyond our conceptual powers, outstripping our ability to describe things in words or images drawn from everyday life, and have to rely on mathematics. We take it as an axiom that reality is stranger than we can ever imagine. Perhaps science, in its own way, is teaching us something about the need to accept that our minds have natural limits. This will have important implications for the way we try to speak about matters of faith.

How then *are* we to talk about God in an age of scientific thought?

I can only speak for myself.

It has never seemed to me that God might or might not exist. The Abominable Snowman might or might not exist; it all depends whether there is one or not. So too, perhaps, the unicorn; that mythical beast may be a storyteller's exaggerated description of a real creature. And aliens from other worlds may exist: one day we shall know. But God?

To ask whether God exists or not, is to imply that he is a *thing* that might – or might not – be 'out there' somewhere, or 'up there', or 'in there'. The question turns him into one more possible inhabitant of my universe, albeit a supernatural inhabitant.

I cannot think of God as a *thing* amongst other things. God for me is the Being in which all things have their existence; my life, my children's lives, the streets we walk in Hammersmith; the planet and its autumn days; the Sun, Moon and stars. We wake up in this realm of reality and cannot sensibly ask whether it exists or not – for here we are. But we *can* ask whether or not this reality is impersonal, uncaring and based upon nothing, or whether it is rooted in what we might tentatively call goodness and delight. I reject the view, both instinctively and thoughtfully, that the evolving universe began with a random and purposeless accident, and that all life is a product of meaningless chemistry.

'God' is the word, the concept, I need for sorting out my experience and my thoughts and for sharing them through conversation; it is the symbol (sometimes the image) that stands for the Being that makes everything about my life real. That Being, I believe, is good and loving and promises me that all will be well. When I use the word God, that says something about my attitude to my life. It might well be possible to speak of these things without using the word God at all.

Faith in the essential goodness of reality demands that we take scientific knowledge seriously. Religious beliefs should not transport us into some other world, some escapist fantasy. They should wake us up to the true nature of *this* world, help us to understand the way things are; make us, in the Buddhist phrase, 'mindful and self-possessed'. To my mind, one of the most appealing figures in Buddhist art is that of the meditating Buddha in Earth-touching mode. He sits in peace, composed, one hand trailing gently to the ground, his wakefulness 'earthed' as it were in reality.

The doctrine of the incarnation in Christianity points the same way. Jesus Christ, as the 'Word made flesh', focusses the mind on physical things; inspires us to view the material universe in sacramental terms. The healing of illness was a tangible expression of his message of compassion; his physical touch brought health to the blind and the outcast leper.

Science helps us understand better who we are; complex creatures built from the same chemistry as the stars, with an almost unfathomable psychology, aspects of which may best be described as spiritual. We are intimately related, through evolution, to the rest of the animal kingdom. Darwinian theory shows us where we have come from, helps us to understand the selfish drives that sometimes cause ruin in our lives (evolutionary baggage described as Original Sin by theology). Science also reveals to us that the laws of nature are open-ended, leaving ample room for choice for both ourselves and for the creative Being in whom we live our lives. To some extent the future is open, not fixed and determined. It does not exist until the Creator draws us into it. In a lovely phrase, Simone Weil described God as 'He in whose wake the world unfolds its days'.

God does not sit above the world, creating it from a distance. He is the inner life of the universe as it grows and evolves. All the laws of nature discovered by science are his laws; the laws that drive biology, creating flowers and people, and the laws of physics that fuel the nuclear furnaces of the suns. Nature is not God, but nature in all its intricate and rich detail expresses the creative will of God. He is at the heart of the process. His presence is intimate to every moment and every event, however minor or apparently insignificant. He is closer to each of us than life or thought.

Science exposes the inevitability of some suffering in the evolving process of life; at the very least, we all grow old and die. Faith in the ultimate goodness of Being may help us to cope with it. It is not always easy being human, whatever attitude we take to it. I can only record that in my own experience the opportunity for delight outweighs everything else.

When I pray, contemplating my life, holding in mind my children, friends and colleagues, I am solitary but I do not feel alone. I feel for the moment that I have poise and equanimity. And when I speak my thoughts and cares inwardly, I feel that I am heard.

Bibliography

Suggestions for Further Reading

Barry, Robert, *A Theory of Almost Everything*, Oneworld 1993

Davies, Paul, *The Fifth Miracle: The Search For the Origin of Life*, Penguin 1998

Forley, Richard, *Life: An Unauthorized Biography. A Natural History of the First 4,000,000 Years of Life on Earth*, Harper Collins 1997

Küng, Hans, *A Global Ethic for Global Politics and Economics*, SCM Press 1997

Lovelock, James, *The Ages of Gaia; A Biography of Our Living Planet*, OUP 1989

Nash, James, *Loving Nature: Ecological Integrity and Christian Responsibility*, Abingdon, Nashville 1992

Polkinghorne, John, *Beyond Science*, CUP 1996

Rifkin, Jeremy, *The Biotech Century*, Gollancz 1998

Ward, Keith, God, *Faith and the New Millennium: Christian Belief in and Age of Science*, Oneworld 1998

Titles Mentioned in the Text

Davies, Paul, *God and the New Physics*, Penguin 1990
Hawking, Stephen, *A Brief History of Time*, Bantam 1988
Huxley, Aldous, *Brave New World*, Chatto 1950
Kundera, Milan, *The Unbearable Lightness of Being*, Faber
1985
von Daniken, Erich, *Chariots of the Gods?*, Corgi 1971
Wurtzel, Elizabeth, *Prozac Nation*, Quartet Books 1996